Preface

The United Kingdom is blessed with landscapes celebrated nationally and internationally for their beauty and biodiversity. Many are protected and enhanced, others, including Durham's Magnesian Limestone areas, have been given relatively little protection and have been exploited with scant consideration as a result.

This book tells a story of a landscape of great rarity. It is also a story of crude exploitation of minerals, habitats and species over many years, culminating in the great ecological and visual damage caused by coal mining, quarrying and waste disposal in former quarries.

It is a story about both the fragility and resilience of the area and tells how it has survived and is being restored following belated recognition of its unique importance. The Turning The Tide Millennium Project, which accelerated the recovery of the Durham coast after more than a hundred years of colliery waste tipping on clifftops and beaches, is evidence of the scale of restoration required.

The purpose of this publication is to further increase awareness of the importance of this limestone landscape and show how it can be handed on to future generations in a state that reflects well on our stewardship.

David Miller

Contents

Thrislington NNR

photo: www.wildstock.co.uk

Introduction

The vast areas of limestone laid down beneath Caribbean-like, shallow, warm seas about 290 million years ago, in what is now northern Europe, have been the basis for prosperous agriculture and rich resources of wildlife and minerals. These lime-rich bedrocks provide fertile soils, which are home to widely diverse habitats and species, abundant water in aquifers and quarried stone for building and chemical processes. Where limestone exists, settlements have thrived as local people have benefited from the exploitation of this rich resource.

Limestone, however, is not a uniform material. It exists in many forms, depending on the fineness of its grains and its chemical content. The Magnesian Limestone of County Durham is one of the rarest and most valuable and the coastal cliffs are unique in the British Isles, home to plant communities not seen together anywhere else in the country. Because as much as two thirds of the national resource of Magnesian Limestone grassland occurs in the North-East of England, it is seen as a jewel in the crown of the region's biodiversity.

This has counted for little in the past and the crude exploitation of mammals, plants and minerals has diminished the area's natural diversity. This book records the loss of several species of mammal and many plant species. Agricultural practice, as is the case almost everywhere in the country, has been a major factor in further depredation. It is, however, the existence of the many limestone quarries on the escarpment, once so crucial to the steel and refractory industries of the North-East, that has provided the refuge for threatened wildlife. Indeed, many of the best sites to explore the wildlife and geology of the area are old quarries.

A further threat to this fragile balance came from pressure to fill the quarries with household and industrial waste. Many have been filled and it is unknown what effect this will have long-term on the quality of water supplies taken from the primary aquifer that underlies the area. Much of this threat has now been contained as regulations for new and extended quarries have become more tightly drawn.

The conservation of the area's resources is a matter of considerable importance and there are yet more uncertainties in the face of climate change that could have a dramatic impact if temperatures rise according to current predictions. Nevertheless, for many years to come the Magnesian Limestone needs to be protected and its wildlife conserved. The recognition by local people of the importance of caring for their unique natural environment is crucial if their communities are to be truly sustainable.

Geology of the Durham Magnesian Limestone

by Brian Young

Introduction

The special landscape of the Durham Magnesian Limestone, with its distinctive flora and fauna and interesting social and economic history, reflects events and processes that shaped this area many millions of years ago. In order to properly appreciate the area as we see it today, we need to understand something of the fascinating story of the rocks beneath our feet.

As the area described in this book comprises the eastern part of the Durham Coalfield, before looking more closely at the Magnesian Limestone itself, and in order to understand the coal mining industry that has been so important in shaping the area, we need to look briefly at these coal-bearing rocks.

Carboniferous Rocks - The Coal Measures

Most of the coal worked in County Durham occurs within a group of rocks known to geologists as the Coal Measures. The coal occurs as thin layers, or seams, sandwiched between beds of other rocks such as shale and sandstone.

These rocks date back to the later part of the Carboniferous Period of earth history, roughly 316 to 295 million years ago. At this time, the area that was to become Great Britain lay almost astride the equator. Vast, low-lying, forest-covered tropical swamps were crossed

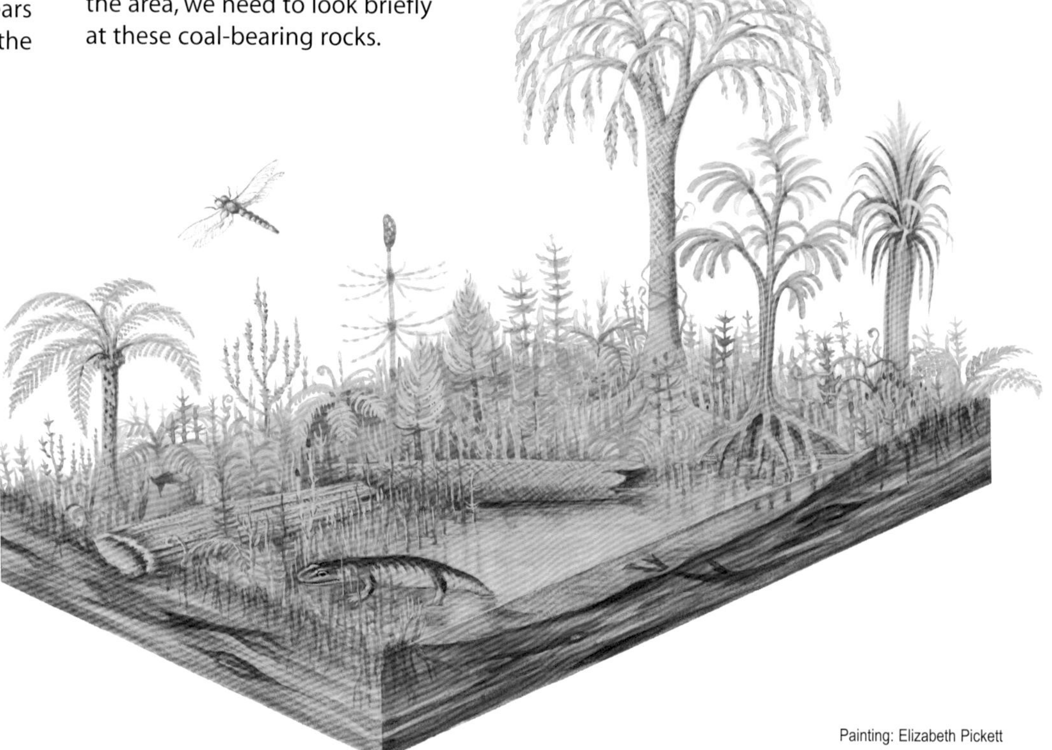

Fig 1. Artist's reconstruction of the type of lush tropical forest in which the vegetation that formed the area's coal seams was deposited, about 310 million years ago

Painting: Elizabeth Pickett

Fig 2. Horizontal section through Durham Coalfield

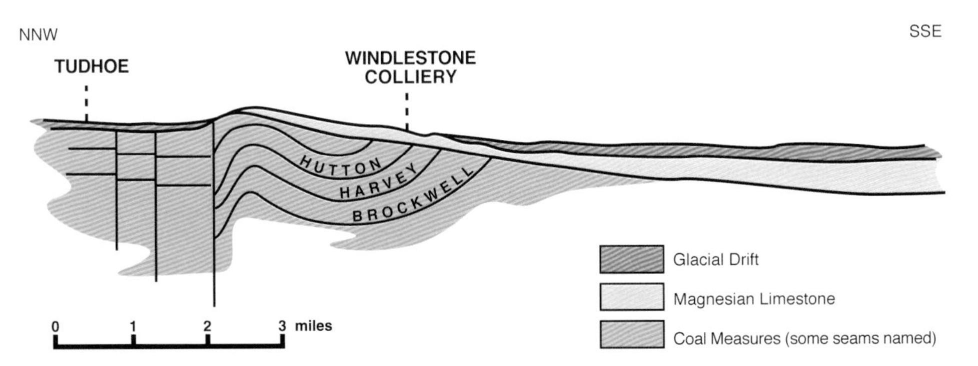

by enormous rivers carrying sand and silt from uplands in the area now occupied by the Scottish Borders and northern North Sea. The forests contained enormous primitive trees, including ancestors of the modern club-mosses and conifers, together with giant ferns and horsetails (Fig 1). True flowering plants had not yet evolved. Animal life included huge newt-like amphibians and giant dragonflies. Thick accumulations of peat and leaf litter on the forest floor became compressed, when buried beneath silt and sand, to form the coal seams we know today. Fossilised leaves and roots from these forests are commonly found in beds of shale within the Coal Measures. Some fine specimens of large petrified logs of a tree known as *Cordiaites* were found several years ago in an opencast coal pit at Priors Close, near Great Lumley.

Near the end of the Carboniferous Period, as this part of the earth's crust shifted northwards, great earth movements squeezed and folded the coal seams and other rocks, pushing them up to form hills and mountains. Weathering and erosion of this new landscape set the scene for the next period of earth history.

Coal Measures rocks lie beneath the Magnesian Limestone and crop out at the surface immediately west of the Magnesian Limestone escarpment (Fig 2). Apart from in the banks of the River Wear at South Hylton, Sunderland and in an old quarry near Shildon, they are rarely exposed in the area, but have been worked in numerous collieries. The best places to see examples of the full range of Coal Measures rocks are old colliery tips and on the beaches of the Durham coast, where large amounts of spoil were once dumped.

Permian Rocks

The episode of earth history that followed the Carboniferous is known as the Permian Period. This lasted from about 295 to 250 million years ago. It was during this time that the Durham Magnesian Limestone was formed, although a few other events were to affect the area before the limestone itself was deposited.

The landscape created at the end of Carboniferous times drifted further northward to between 10 to 30 degrees north of the equator during Permian times. Northern Europe was then one of the world's great deserts in which sand, formed by the wearing away of the hills, accumulated as long belts of dunes. We see these today as the 'Yellow Sands', that are extensively worked for building sand in quarries around Quarrington, Coxhoe and Ferryhill (Fig 3). Evidence of their wind-borne origin may be seen in the huge dune-bedding so clearly visible in quarry faces, and in the perfectly rounded 'millet seed' shape of individual grains. The sands continue at

***Fig 3.** Permian Yellow Sands, fossilised sand dunes, being worked for building sand at Crime Rigg Quarry, Sherburn*

Photo: Brian Young

Fig 4. *Extent of the Zechstein Sea*

depth beneath the limestone where, because they are so porous and typically contain huge quantities of water, they presented major problems in sinking colliery shafts. Beneath parts of the North Sea, these same sands are important reservoirs for oil and gas.

This desert landscape was eventually flooded as the waters of the Zechstein Sea, a precursor of the modern North Sea, spread rapidly across the area, reaching as far as the present day eastern edge of the Pennines (Fig 4). Unlike the present-day North Sea, this was a warm sea that dried up almost completely on several occasions.

The earliest limestone to be deposited, probably about 270 million years ago, was a thin bed of dark grey bituminous shaly limestone, known in North-East England as the Marl Slate (Fig 5). The composition and fossil content of this rock indicate its deposition in stagnant water, perhaps between 200 to 300 metres deep. The Marl Slate is internationally famous for its locally abundant fauna of beautifully preserved fish, especially species of *Palaeoniscus* (Fig 6) together with rarer reptile, amphibian and plant fossils. Numerous magnificent specimens have been collected from quarries in the Sunderland area, at Quarrington, Ferryhill and elsewhere. Middridge Quarry is famous for specimens of early reptiles such as *Protosaurus* and *Adelosaurus* and Eppleton Quarry, near Hetton-le-Hole, yielded one of only a handful of European specimens of the early gliding reptile *Coelurosaurus*.

Photo: Brian Young

Fig 5. *The Marl Slate (the thinly-bedded grey rock above the hammer) resting on Yellow Sands. Old Quarrington Quarry, County Durham.*

Fig 6. *Palaeoniscus longissimus - a fossilised fish from the Marl Slate, collected at Thrislington, County Durham.*

Engraving from King W. 1850. Monograph of the Permian Fossils of England. Palaeontographical Society Monograph reproduced by courtesy of the Palaeontographical Society.

Above the Marl Slate occurs a rather complex succession of limestones of different compositions and textures, formed in rather varying conditions beneath the waters of the Zechstein Sea, and collectively termed the Magnesian Limestone (Fig 7). Whereas true limestone consists almost entirely of the mineral calcite ($CaCO_3$), many of the limestones here in east Durham contain large amounts, or may consist almost exclusively, of the magnesium-rich mineral dolomite ($CaMg(CO_3)_2$). Such rocks are often called dolomitic limestones or magnesian limestones. It is important here to differentiate between the rock type 'magnesian limestone' and the formal geological unit called the Magnesian Limestone which, although including much magnesian limestone, also includes other less magnesium-rich limestones. It is almost certainly this abundance of magnesium that accounts for the area's characteristic Magnesian Limestone flora.

Being rather more resistant to erosion than most of the underlying Coal Measures rocks, the Magnesian Limestone typically forms a prominent west-facing escarpment overlooking the central part of County Durham (Fig 8).

Fig 7 (top inset). *Limestone typical of the lower part of the Magnesian Limestone, Chilton Quarry, Ferryhill.*

Fig 8 (right). *The Magnesian Limestone escarpment overlooking the Coal Measures outcrop, Houghton Cut, Sunderland*

Fig 9. *Vertical limestone cliffs and sea stacks near Marsden*

On the coast, the Magnesian Limestone typically forms vertical cliffs, commonly with caves and sea stacks reflecting differing degrees of resistance to erosion (Fig 9).

The details of the Magnesian Limestone succession need not concern us here. However, the lower beds of limestone, exposed in numerous quarries and road cuttings on the escarpment, show clear roughly horizontal bedding. Although fossils are generally scarce in most of these rocks, a feature of the Durham Magnesian Limestone is the presence of a well-preserved barrier reef, formed close to the Zechstein coastline. Unlike most modern reefs, this was built not of corals, but of the skeletons of 'moss-like animals' known as bryozoans, together with a wealth of shells (Figs 10 & 11). The reef today forms a conspicuous line of hills extending from Downhill at West Boldon, through Humbledon and Tunstall Hills in Sunderland, to Beacon Hill at Easington and Blackhall Rocks on the modern coastline. In places, a variety of reef-forming animals are strikingly preserved, though in many places recrystallisation of the limestone has destroyed or obscured these.

Fig 10. *Fenestella retiformis - a fossilised bryozoan from the Magnesian Limestone reef, collected at Humbledon Hill, Sunderland.*
Engraving from King W. 1850. Monograph of the Permian Fossils of England. Palaeontographical Society Monograph reproduced by courtesy of the Palaeontographical Society.

Other distinctive limestones include the 'Flexible Limestone' exposed on the coast north of Sunderland, so called because its very thin layers can often be bent like cardboard. The Sunderland area is also famous for the 'Concretionary Limestone', often referred to locally as the 'Cannon Ball Limestone' (Fig 12). This odd-looking rock, which is believed to have formed by complex recrystallisation of the original limestone, commonly consists

Fig 11 (top inset). *Reef Limestone exposed at Humbledon Hill, Sunderland during the widening of the A690 road in the 1970s. Now unfortunately concealed beneath a retaining wall.*

Fig 12 (bottom inset). *Typical 'Cannon Ball' Limestone exposed in Fulwell Quarries Sunderland.*

Fig 13 (right). *Star-shaped groups of calcite crystals in the Concretionary Limestone exposed at Marsden Old Quarry LNR.*

of masses of spherical concretions which vary in size from a small pea to a small football. In places, the concretions occur as fan-shaped aggregates of narrow rods or as star-shaped groups of calcite crystals. Spectacular sections of this rock are exposed at Marsden Old Quarry LNR and on the coast at Hendon, south of Sunderland, with smaller exposures in the sea cliffs near Crimdon.

Many parts of the Magnesian Limestone have been worked as a local building stone, but larger quarries continue to be quarried to supply limestone and dolomite to the construction and chemical industries

Periodic evaporation of water in the Zechstein Sea caused minerals dissolved in the water to crystallise, forming thick beds of anhydrite ($CaSO_4$), gypsum ($CaSO_4.2H_2O$) and, more rarely rock salt (NaCl) and potash (KCl). These minerals are collectively known as evaporites. Anhydrite was formerly mined at Hartlepool and Billingham, for making cement and chemicals. Rock salt is still worked by pumping brine from boreholes in the Hartlepool area, and potash is mined at Boulby, south of the area. Near the surface these soluble minerals normally dissolved millions of years ago, causing the overlying limestone to collapse. The rubble-like appearance of much of the limestone exposed on the Durham coast is a result of this process of 'collapse brecciation'.

From late Permian times until as recently as two million years ago, the story of this part of County Durham falls largely silent.

Quaternary Geology

Roughly two million years ago, a worldwide episode of global cooling caused ice sheets more than one kilometre thick to extend southwards across northern Europe on several occasions, scouring the landscape and leaving great spreads of glacial debris in their wake. Between long cold spells the climate became at least as mild as it is today, only to be followed by a return to cold conditions.

Most widespread and conspicuous of the deposits formed at this period is till or boulder clay. This comprises a heterogeneous mixture of boulders, sand and clay dumped by the ice sheets. Boulders of distinctive rock types, known as 'erratics', reveal the direction of ice flow. Over much of east Durham there is evidence of ice bringing rocks from the Cheviots, Pennines and Lake District although, close to the coast, distinctive Scandinavian rock types reveal ice flow from across the North Sea. A prominent

Fig 15. The 'Raised Beach' exposed in the cliffs above Shippersea Bay, Easington

Photo: Brian Young

Fig 14. *Boulder Clay forming the upper grass-covered slopes above the Magnesian Limestone near Blackhall Rocks*

Photo: www.wildstock.co.uk

belt of rather hummocky country between Easington and Hartlepool has been interpreted as a morainic deposit that may have formed near the meeting of two ice streams. Whereas boulder clay covers large parts of the area, it is most clearly seen as the brown stony clay capping the limestone in the coastal cliffs (Fig 14). A wide selection of 'erratic' blocks can be collected from these beaches.

Deposits of sand and gravel, and locally pockets of silt and clay deposited in temporary lakes, also occur locally either resting upon, or inter-bedded, with boulder clay.

Over time, the land surface became depressed by the enormous weight of ice. As this finally melted, about 11,000 years ago, the land rose. Combined with the release of vast quantities of glacial meltwater this resulted in fluctations in sea level and repeatedly changed the position of the Durham coast. Distinctive deposits formed at this time include the 'raised beach' containing 38000 year old shells, preserved about 30 metres above the modern beach at Easington (Fig 15) and the submerged forest of 8-9,000 year old tree trunks about 15 metres below present sea level near Hartlepool.

The comparatively sudden release of huge amounts of meltwater, combined with the gradual rise in the land, cut the deep canyon-like gorges we see today as the coastal denes. Other channels, cut by meltwaters, may be seen inland near Kelloe (Fig 16) and at Ferryhill.

References

Because the Durham Magnesian Limestone and adjoining areas have long been the subject of geological research, a very large technical literature exists. In a publication of this sort it is appropriate to list only a handful of the most important or most readily accessible of these texts. The reader interested in accessing more specialised descriptions is directed to the very substantial reference lists contained in the publications listed here.

JOHNSON, G.A.L. 1970 (compiler). Geology of Durham County. *Transactions of the Natural History Society of Northumberland, Durham and Newcastle upon Tyne*, Vol. 41, No. 1.

JOHNSON, G.A.L. 1995 (editor). Robson's geology of North East England. *Transactions of the Natural History Society of Northumbria*, Vol. 56, Part 5.

MILLS, D.A.C. and HULL, J.H. 1976. Geology of the country around Barnard Castle. *Memoir of the Geological Survey of Great Britain*, Sheet 32 (England & Wales)

SMITH, D.B. 1994. Geology of the country around Sunderland. *Memoir of the British Geological Survey*, Sheet 21 (England & Wales)

SMITH, D.B. 1995. Marine Permian of England. *Geological Conservation Review Series* No. 8. Chapman & Hall, London

SMITH, D.B. and FRANCIS, E.H. 1967. Geology of the country between Durham and West Hartlepool. *Memoir of the Geological Survey of Great Britain*, Sheet 27 (England & Wales)

Photo: www.wildstock.co.uk

Fig 16. *Glacial meltwater cut channel near Kelloe*

The Social and Economic Development of the Magnesian Limestone

by David Butler

Seaton Holme, a medieval manor house in the agricultural settlement of Easington, c1950 (DCRO D/CL 5/1026)

To understand the history of the area, an understanding of its geology and ecology is also necessary. The often bleak and windswept Magnesian Limestone plateau is geologically distinct from the area to the west, and although its social and economic development broadly mirrored the remainder of the county, in the east developments occurred at different times and followed different routes, thus giving the area a uniqueness which persists today.

In prehistoric times, the plateau was covered with a forest in which different types of trees predominated as conditions changed. Because the soils were relatively dry and easy to work, the clearance of the forest preceded other areas of the county and by Roman times the plateau was probably an area of relatively intensive arable farming on the better soils, with widespread pastoral activity. Woodland would have been mainly restricted to the steep slopes of the denes and to areas of heavier, wetter soils.

By 1000 AD a pattern of communal working of the land was established, with large arable town-fields subdivided into unfenced strips which changed hands regularly and a population largely living in clearly defined settlements.

A map of the Magnesian Limestone plateau reveals a landscape of relatively small settlements, falling into two broad categories. On one hand there are those with an irregular layout and central village greens, such as Easington, which, if studied on the ground, will be found to have buildings which pre-date the nineteenth century, with, usually, a medieval parish church. These settlements came into existence as agricultural villages, and largely still retain an agricultural base, although the map will also show evidence of agricultural villages which have not survived, such as Yoden, which had become deserted by the sixteenth century.

In many cases the distinctive ridge-and-furrow ploughing pattern, often cutting across modern field boundaries, can be found near these settlements. The seventeenth century saw the dispersion of the population with the change to a pattern of individually owned and worked holdings on which isolated

Aerial photograph of the earthworks of Yoden deserted village at Peterlee, 1968 (DCRO CC/X 172/44 no.428)

farmsteads were built. This allowed farmers to concentrate on the type of farming best suited to a particular location. Once the coal industry began to develop in east Durham, then its requirements, particularly fodder and summer grazing for pit ponies, led to the specialisation of some farms.

The other group of settlements are characterised by the more formalised terraces of nineteenth and twentieth century housing and are the colliery villages of the east Durham plateau. In much of County Durham, coal seams lie close to the surface and were relatively easy to exploit. However, in the east of the county, the 'concealed coalfield', the seams are overlaid by the Magnesian Limestone, and for many years there were doubts that coal existed beneath the limestone. From the end of the eighteenth century, however, it was generally accepted that coal would be found although it was believed that it would be low grade and expensive to obtain.

Eventually, declining production in the exposed coalfield and increasing demand for coal directed interest to east Durham, at a time when technological developments provided solutions to the problems of ventilation and drainage and made it possible to work at greater depths. The capital requirements for these new sinkings were beyond the capacity of individual landowners, and this led to the establishment of joint-stock mining companies with greater financial resources. The first successful attempt to breach the Magnesian Limestone capping came with the Hetton Coal Company's sinking of Hetton Lyons Colliery in 1822. With proof of the existence of good quality coal, collieries began to spread over the plateau. The general trend was eastwards and, in the twentieth century, deep coastal pits were sunk which worked eight kilometres out under the North Sea. These pits represented the final phase of the coal industry in Durham, and the county's last colliery, Wearmouth, closed in 1993.

Horden tipping point for colliery waste, near Warren House Point, c1950 (DCRO URA 133/5)

Coal only becomes saleable if it can be moved economically to its markets, and this meant cheap transport to the coast. This was accomplished by railways with a mix of locomotive and rope haulage, as used on the Hetton Colliery Railway, the first railway in the world designed to be operated by steam locomotives. The growing number of collieries meant the development of a network of lines, mostly owned by individual colliery companies. With the demise of the coal industry went the closure of the railways, and all that now remains is the coastal line, completed in 1905. The old railway routes have often survived as walk-ways or simply as undeveloped corridors and as such, provide refuges for the unique flora and wildlife of the plateau, and reservoirs from which that flora can begin to re-establish itself.

There was no pool of labour available locally to work in the growing coal industry, and the need to house the immigrant mining families led to the growth of the ubiquitous pit village, with terraces of houses constructed by the colliery company, chapels, allotments and basic shops. The east Durham pit villages tended to be larger than those in the west and more systematically laid out, but since they had no rationale for their existence other than the colliery, the closure of

Seaham Harbour, with the 3rd Marquis of Londonderry's original dock of 1831 in the foreground, c1950
(DCRO D/CL 5/1984)

the latter inevitably led to economic problems. One response, which was suggested in Easington Rural District Council's 1946 publication, *Farewell Squalor*, was the creation of Peterlee, a new town named after the Durham miners' leader, to provide better centralised social and cultural facilities than could be achieved by piecemeal additions to colliery villages.

The coastal collieries did not create pit heaps but dumped their waste at sea. Until World War II the sea was able to deal with this waste and an equilibrium was broadly achieved, but with increased output and mechanisation the balance could not be maintained, and the result was 12 kilometres of the coast devastated by colliery waste, which, perversely, had the effect of protecting the Magnesian Limestone cliffs from erosion. One of the benefits of the cessation of deep mining has been the chance to restore the coast to its former state, and the Turning the Tide clean-up project has removed some of the spoil and the sea is dealing with much of the remainder. The project has also reclaimed the colliery sites and permitted the acquisition, for the benefit of the public, of areas of cliff top arable land, much of which had been meadow before the demands of World War II for food production led to its ploughing-up. It is now being returned to pasture with regimes which encourage the re-establishment of the unique Magnesian Limestone flora. Another legacy from World War II can be found in the surviving pill-boxes and anti-tank blocks which were erected to protect the area from invasion.

World War II pill-box at Hawthorn Dene

Photo: www.wildstock.co.uk

The head gear and surface structures of Easington Colliery sunk in 1899 and closed in 1993
(DCRO D/CL 5/1046)

Castle Eden 'Castle', built in the mid-eighteenth century for Rowland Burdon the elder, 1886
(DCRO D/CL 5/491)

Coal is not the only extractive industry which has flourished on the Magnesian Limestone plateau. The limestone itself was, and remains, a useful raw material and the surface of the plateau is dissected by large quarries. Much of the limestone has been despatched to Teesside to be used in the iron and steel industry, as a flux in the furnaces and for furnace lining. It is also used for constructional purposes (road stone, hardcore and aggregate), and in chemical and pharmaceutical manufacture. In the past, it has been used as a building material and also converted into slaked lime for agricultural use in limekilns. On a smaller scale, and less disruptive to the landscape, the overlying glacial deposits have been worked for clay, sand and gravel at a number of locations.

Major elements in the East Durham landscape owe their survival to the large landowners who acquired estates in the eighteenth and nineteenth centuries; the areas which they preserved for their own enjoyment have survived and are reservoirs for the natural flora of the plateau. The Burdon family purchased land at Castle Eden in 1758, including Castle Eden Dene which they landscaped and laid out with promenades (such as Miss Mary's Walk) which could be enjoyed from The Castle. This ensured the preservation of the Dene and its unique collection of habitats, but also provided an area which was open to the public from around 1850. The Andersons then the Pembertons occupied the Hawthorn Estate, with Hawthorn Dene, from the 1830s and were responsible for some of the woodland planting which still survives. Hawthorn Towers was demolished in 1969, but its site can still be appreciated. The influence of the Londonderry family was more in what they built than what they preserved. The 3rd marquis had grandiose plans for his new town of Seaham, most of which did not materialise, but the town and harbour are his memorial, and the family remained major landowners in the area until the second half of the twentieth century.

Quarrying operations at Thrislington Quarry 2006 (Right)

Photo: www.wildstock.co.uk

Current Status

by Julie Stobbs

Limestone areas tend to be of special interest for wild plants and the Durham Magnesian Limestone Natural Area is no exception. Within Britain the solid geology of Magnesian Limestone underlies an area of about 1,200 square kilometres. This extends in a narrow band, no greater than eight kilometres wide, from Nottinghamshire up to Yorkshire, and where it reaches Darlington it fans out into a much broader belt covering eastern County Durham and a significant part of Sunderland and South Tyneside.

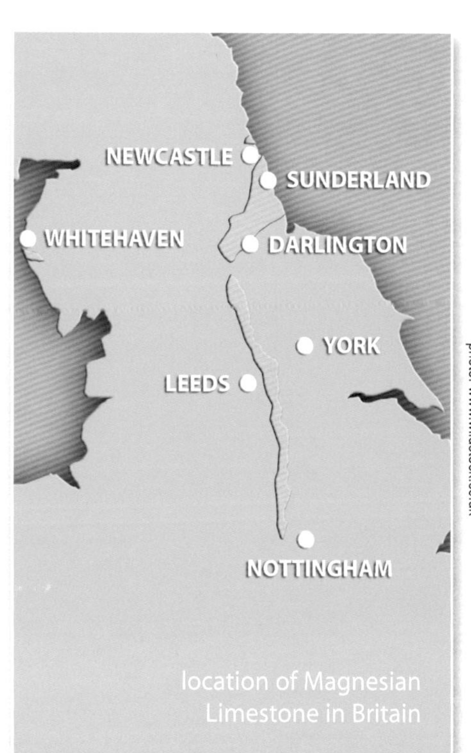

location of Magnesian Limestone in Britain

In excess of 90% of the Magnesian Limestone is overlain by "drift" deposits from later periods of geological history. The depth of the drift determines how far the Magnesian Limestone can influence plants growing on the surface.

As much as two thirds of the UK resource of Magnesian Limestone grassland occurs in North East England and because of its internationally recognised importance, it can be seen as a "jewel in the crown" of the region's biodiversity. A large number of organisations with nature conservation interests are working together to ensure that the best sites are protected and that others are enhanced through appropriate management.

Within the North-East there are four National Nature Reserves on the Magnesian Limestone, Thrislington Plantation, Cassop Vale, Castle Eden Dene and the Durham Coast. Of these, all except Cassop are also designated as Special Areas of Conservation under the European Union's Habitats Directive.

Natural England has also designated 48 Sites of Special Scientific Interest (SSSIs), which are in varying ownership but have legal protection under the Wildlife and Countryside Act 1981. Of the 307 hectares of Magnesian Limestone grassland in the North-East, 279 hectares are protected in this way. At least 132 further sites are designated as "second tier" Sites of Nature Conservation Importance (SNCIs), an unusually high density. SNCIs normally have some protection through the local authority planning system.

Grasslands

Within the North-East, the grasslands of greatest interest are scattered throughout the Magnesian Limestone Natural Area with the better sites on the west-facing escarpment on the coast or in the central area around the National

Herb-rich grassland at Hawthorn Dene

photo: www.wildstock.co.uk

Nature Reserves at Thrislington Plantation and Cassop Vale. It is at these two sites, together with the nearby Town Kelloe Bank SSSI, that the best examples of *primary* Magnesian Limestone grassland occur, areas of original agriculturally-unimproved herb-rich grassland on shallow Magnesian Limestone soils. Here the conditions are most appropriate for a remarkable assemblage of plant species, many of which are highly attractive when in flower during the summer months.

The assemblage seen at sites such as Thrislington Plantation is particularly significant because it includes plants of northern affinities, which tend to occur on the older Carboniferous limestones of areas like the North Pennines and Cumbria, growing with plants of southern origins, which are more typical of the chalk and limestones of southern England. The Magnesian Limestone can, therefore, be seen as something of an "ecological bridge" between these two types of plant community. Examples of northern species include Blue Moor Grass (*Sesleria caerulea*), Bird's Eye Primrose (*Primula farinosa*) and

photo: www.wildstock.co.uk

Carpet of Rockrose
Thrislington NNR

Hawthorn Dene

photo: www.wildstock.co.uk

Mountain Everlasting (*Antennaria dioica*) while some of the southern species growing near the northern limit of their distribution include Upright Brome (*Bromopsis erecta*) and the rare and beautiful blue Perennial Flax (*Linum perenne*). The latter is one of the most striking components of Thrislington National Nature Reserve and was protected "in situ" from quarrying when other parts of the herb-rich grassland were only saved through a transplantation scheme in the 1980s.

Rather more numerous than the primary grasslands are secondary grasslands, most of which owe their origins to the recolonisation of old quarry workings but which can also occur on habitats such as roadside verges and former railway lines. Many have developed an interesting flora of species which flourish on the rudimentary soils and orchid displays can be spectacular. It is critical that appropriate management is carried out to conserve them and arrest the process of natural succession. On both primary and secondary Magnesian Limestone grassland, management requirements such as scrub removal, cutting and introduction of grazing can be essential to the maintenance of a herb-rich sward.

Town Kelloe Bank

Coastal Denes

Within the coastal strip the East-West aligned coastal denes support some of the most natural woodland in North East England. The denes were created by glacial meltwater at the end of the last ice age and are steep-sided and relatively inaccessible. Typically, Ash (*Fraxinus excelsior*) and Wych Elm (*Ulmus glabra*) flourish while Yew (*Taxus baccata*) is an interesting additional component at Castle Eden Dene.

photo: www.wildstock.co.uk

Bird's eye primrose

photo: Ian Armstrong

Cassop Vale

photo: www.wildstock.co.uk

The ground flora of the denes contains many species which are indicators of their ancient status and species normally more common in the West, such as Hart's Tongue fern, flourish in the humid dene bottoms.

Uniqueness

Not only is Magnesian Limestone grassland unique to Britain but one of its main plant communities is unique to the North-East, characterised by the presence of Blue Moor Grass (*Sesleria caerulea*) (so called because of its amazing blue sheen in the early csummer) and the delicate Small Scabious (*Scabiosa columbaria*).

photo: www.wildstock.co.uk
Small scabious

Bearing in mind that geological features such as the fossil reef and Cannon Ball Limestones are also unique to the area, the claim for its importance is certainly justified. Both Magnesian Limestone grassland and lowland Ash woodland have been identified as habitats deserving of special conservation measures in action plans produced for the area of old County Durham.

Given the special interest of the Magnesian Limestone grasslands, it is fair to say that the best of the grasslands, such as Thrislington, display a degree of interest that makes them "more than the sum of their parts". Many local people, with due justification, consider it a privilege to live in close proximity to these special habitats and to be involved in their conservation.

photo: www.wildstock.co.uk
Early purple orchid

Flora and Vegetation of the Magnesian Limestone

by John Durkin

Northern marsh orchid

The character and history of the Magnesian Limestone has produced special grassland, woodland, wetlands and coastal areas that support a range of uncommon plants.

Grasslands

There are very few original areas of Magnesian Limestone grassland remaining. Those that survive are some of the richest grasslands and are mostly protected within SSSIs. Secondary grasslands are much more numerous, and, although they lack some of the notable plants of the original grasslands, they are often quite rich in other special species. Some of these secondary grasslands originate from land affected by quarrying, road construction or other developments. Others are original grasslands that have been ploughed for arable crops then allowed to revert to pasture.

Woodlands

The first farmers cleared most of the woodland from the Magnesian Limestone escarpment, leaving only small woods on the steepest slopes. Large woodlands only survived at the coast, where the rugged terrain of the denes made farming impractical. This is where most of the characteristic woodland plants are still to be found.

The coastal denes are the main habitat for many of our native woodland plants, including trees such as Yew and Small-leaved Lime, shrubs such as Spindle and Spurge Laurel, and flowers such as Lily of the Valley, Bird's Nest Orchid and Herb Paris.

Wetlands

The porous nature of the limestone reduces the likelihood of ponds and marshes forming on its surface. Only the presence of glacial boulder clay here and there creates a waterproof liner for wetlands. Consequently, ponds are very scarce on the limestone, and most are in old clay pits. They often have a richer flora than ponds on the coal measures. Particularly important are "flushes", which are grasslands on sloping banks, with calcareous water trickling downhill, the main habitats for Butterwort, Grass of Parnassus, Bird's Eye Primrose, and Lesser Clubmoss.

Coast

The coast is a particularly interesting habitat, contrasting with the inland limestone. It has a milder, wetter, more frost-free climate, and the limestone habitats are less fragmented than inland.

The cliffs and headlands have a mixture of coastal and limestone species, including Sea Spleenwort, Dropwort and Thrift. Small flushes on the sea banks support Bird's Eye Primrose, Grass of Parnassus, and Yellow Flag Iris. Drier areas support Round-leaved Wintergreen and Juniper.

Characteristic flowers of the Magnesian Limestone include:

Blue Moor Grass (*Sesleria caerulea)* is the characteristic grass of the Magnesian Limestone. It flowers and sets seed early in the season and is able to grow in very thin soils that dry out later in the summer. It is able to colonise new sites, so it is found both in original grasslands and in man-made habitats such as roadside verges and disused quarries. It also grows on the Carboniferous limestones of Upper Teesdale. The Durham limestones support about one quarter of the British populations of this nationally scare plant.

Time and place to see it - April to September at any of the inland nature reserves. It is less frequent at the coast.

Sea Spleenwort (*Asplenium marinum)* grows only in the sea spray zone on the Magnesian Limestone cliffs. It is an evergreen fern related to the Hart's Tongue, adapted to grow in these difficult conditions. Its preferred habitat is rocks soaked with spray at every high tide, where even Thrift and Sea Mayweed cannot grow. It particularly likes the harder limestone layers with pits and hollows, where young plants can establish themselves. The rapid erosion of our coastal cliffs in recent years has resulted in the loss of some of the colonies of this fern, but its preference for harder rocks ensures that some will survive.

Blue moor grass

photo: Keith Cunningham

Bee orchid

photo: John Bridges

Perennial flax

photo: www.wildstock.co.uk

Birds eye primrose

Thrift

Cowslip

Time and place to see it - At any time of the year, in the bays north of the caves at Blackhall Rocks, and on the north side of Shippersea Point.

Perennial Flax (*Linum perenne)* is one of the rarest and most beautiful of the flowers of the Magnesian Limestone. The blue flowers are at their best at the same time as yellow Rockrose and purple Thyme, making a colourful display. It is easy to find when in flower at its two remaining sites, as it usually flowers prolifically. Occasional plants can be found with white flowers.

Perennial Flax has declined from six sites in the 1960s, down to two now. The other sites were lost due to the encroachment of gorse and hawthorn scrub, and by burning of the scrub. However, it is abundant in its two remaining sites, which are both protected as nature reserves. Recently, it has begun to spread to neighbouring sites.

Time and place to see it - In June and July, at Harton Down Hill near South Shields and at Thrislington.

Bird's Eye Primrose (*Primula farinosa).* Named for the bright yellow centre of its rose-pink flowers, this small primrose has its main habitat on the limestone hills of the north Pennines. Like many other plants of the northern limestone, it also grows on the lowland Magnesian Limestone. Here it prefers original grasslands, especially where there is some flushing of water in the soil. This is one of the scarcest of the Magnesian Limestone habitats, and the one that has declined the most in the twentieth century. Bird's Eye Primrose is now a scarce plant found in only a handful of lowland sites.

Time and place to see it - May and June at Town Kelloe Bank, Thrislington and Blackhall Rocks.

Butterwort (*Pinguicula vulgaris)* grows on very poor damp soils, even on almost bare rock, because it supplements its food supply by catching insects. Sticky glands on the leaves trap the insects, the soft parts of which are then dissolved and absorbed by the plant. The yellow-green rosettes of leaves are distinctive.

Time and place to see it - Wingate Quarry L.N.R. from May to July.

Cowslip (*Primula veris)*. Most of the flowers of the Magnesian Limestone bloom in mid summer, but cowslips, common on all of the reserves, are one of the earliest spring flowers. They flower at the same time as the Blue Moor Grass, and, on some reserves, Early Purple Orchids. Cowslips are much more adaptable than their relative, the Bird's Eye Primrose, and can commonly be seen on roadside verges, especially along the A19. The Cowslip is the grassland relative of the woodland Primrose. These two flowers can be found together on some reserves, such as Cassop Vale, together with hybrids of intermediate form and colours.

Time and place to see it - Any of the Magnesian Limestone reserves, in April and May.

Common Rockrose, (*Helianthemum nummularium)*. The bright yellow flowers of this small perennial shrub can be seen in most of the reserves, in rough grassland, disused quarries and scrub. It is very important in Durham, because it is the foodplant of the caterpillar of the Northern Brown Argus butterfly. Sheltered sites with large amounts of

photo: John Bridges

Butterwort

photo: John Bridges

Butterwort

photo: www.wildstock.co.uk

Rockrose

Typical Magnesian Limestone meadow

Rockrose provide the main remaining habitats for this butterfly, so some reserves have managed to increase the amount of rockrose.

Time and place to see it - Any of the Magnesian Limestone reserves, from late May through to September.

Greater Knapweed (*Centaurea scabiosa*). One of the tallest and most striking of the summer flowers on the Magnesian Limestone, found in a mixture of habitats including roadside verges and quarries. The tall, purple-red flowers are often accompanied by the blue-violet flowers of Field Scabious, (*Knautia arvensis*).

Time and place to see it - Any of the nature reserves, from June to August.

Hart's Tongue (*Phyllitis scolopendrium*). This evergreen fern covers the ground in large areas of the coastal denes. It is unusual for a fern in having an undivided, strap-shaped frond, instead of the finely divided fronds of the other woodland ferns. Some of the Hawthorn Dene plants have Y-shaped, forked fronds. The spores are produced from the "sori", brown lines on the underside of the fronds.

Time and place to see it - All year round, close to the streams in the coastal denes.

Dark Red Helleborine (*Epipactis atrorubens*). Of all the flowers of the Magnesian Limestone, this orchid is very special because most of its British population is in Durham Wildlife Trust reserves. These populations are carefully monitored each year. The Dark Red Helleborine prefers bare ground with rocks and very little soil, so it is well suited to growing in the disused quarries. It is not as showy as the more colourful orchids, at first sight, but it repays closer inspection.

photo: Keith Cunningham
photo: Dave Mitchell
Lady's Slipper Orchid
Hart's tongue fern

Time and place to see it - From June to August in the Durham Wildlife Trust reserves at Bishop Middleham Quarry and Raisby Hill Grassland.

Orchids are very common on the Magnesian Limestone, particularly in the disused quarries. Some of these orchids, such as the Common Spotted and the Northern Marsh, are frequent in other habitats. Special to the limestone are three less common species, the Fragrant, Pyramidal, and Bee orchids.

These are very well named, Fragrant having a strong sweet scent, Pyramidal having a cone shaped flower and Bee Orchids having florets that are said to resemble bees. All of these characteristics are to assist in pollination by insects. The numbers of orchids that flower in any given year can vary enormously, from a few dozen to many hundreds, depending upon the weather.

Time and place to see them - Any of the Magnesian Limestone reserves that include disused quarries or limestone grasslands. Most orchids flower in June and July.

The Lady's Slipper Orchid (*Cypripedium calceolus*). Is one of Britain's rarest and most beautiful orchids. Lady's Slipper once grew in a number of woodlands on limestone in the north of England, including in Hawthorn and Castle Eden Denes. It became extinct, mostly due to collecting, except at one Yorkshire site. The last Durham Lady's Slippers were carefully guarded, but the last one was seen in flower in 1926.

Young plants from Yorkshire have now been specially grown in greenhouses and re-introduced to Durham's coastal denes by Natural England.

Time and place to see it - When the young plants mature, it may be possible for some of them to be shown to visitors in the nature reserves where they are growing.

The Durham Coast

by Dave Mitchell

photo: www.wildstock.co.uk

photo: Dave Mitchell

Unique sea cliff vegetation at Marsden Bay

The Durham Coast is unique in terms of Britain's flora and vegetation.

Although it only covers a 30-kilometre section of coastline from South Shields to Crimdon, it supports one third of all Magnesian Limestone grassland in this country and is the only place where Magnesian Limestone rock creates coastal outcrops. The area is also located on a divide between the warmer drier south of Britain and the cool, wet north. These factors have resulted in a unique and internationally-important assemblage of plants and habitats that can be readily observed as described in the following sections.

Exposed sea cliffs

at The Leas and Whitburn Coastal Park, South Shields

Some of the most exposed sea cliffs along the Durham Coast occur here. Battered by gale force winds and winter storms laden with salt spray, the cliffs are exposed to the full might of the North Sea and a highly specialised flora has developed in response to the harsh conditions.

Plants with thick fleshy leaves, resembling those of succulents, cling to the cliffs where few others can survive. The leaves help to reduce water loss in the salty soils and are less vulnerable to wind damage. Most obvious are the beautiful carpets of Sea Pink or 'Thrift' (*Armeria maritima*), which derives its names from its colour and habitat and from the fact that it 'thrives' or remains green throughout the year.

Another evergreen specialist is Common Scurvygrass (*Cochlearia officinalis*) which is not actually a grass but a small member of the cabbage family. It has a high content of vitamin C and, before the discovery of citrus fruits, was eaten by sailors on long sea voyages to prevent them developing scurvy, a disease caused by vitamin C deficiency. Other salt-tolerant specialists to be seen here include Sea Plantain (*Plantago maritima*), Buckshorn Plantain (*Plantago coronopus*) and the locally rare fern Sea Spleenwort (*Asplenium marinum*).

photo: Dave Mitchell

Exposed sea cliffs at The Leas, South Shields

Sheltered coastline

at Castle Eden Dene, Horden

In direct contrast to the previous site, much of the Durham sea cliffs are protected behind artificial raised beaches formed after the dumping of colliery wastes into the sea last century. This helps to shelter the vegetation

photo: Dave Mitchell

Sea cliffs protected behind foreshore wastes at the mouth of Castle Eden Dene, Horden

from the direct effects of the sea and plants find further shelter in the numerous gills and denes that dissect the coastline. The largest and most accessible of these is at the mouth of Castle Eden Dene.

Its sheltered conditions help support a diverse and robust grassland vegetation, including Black Knapweed (*Centaurea nigra*), Greater Knapweed (*Centaurea scabiosa*), Devil's Bit Scabious (*Succisa pratensis*) and Wild Thyme (*Thymus polytrichus*), all of which support diverse insect life. Of particular note are the patches of common Rockrose (*Helianthemum nummularium*) that support important coastal colonies of the Northern Brown Argus butterfly (*Aricia artaxerxes*).

all plant photos: Dave Mitchell (unless credited)

Buck's horn plantain

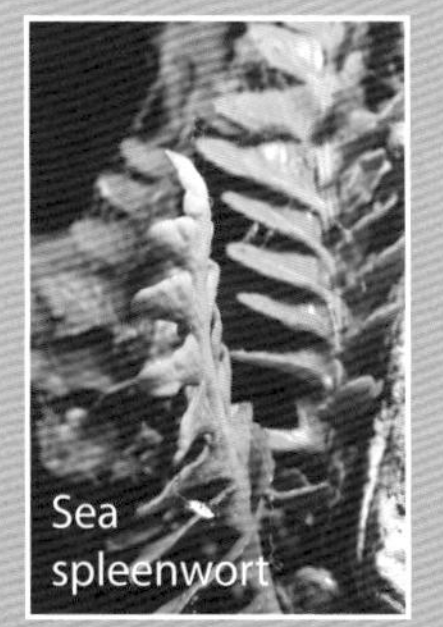

Sea spleenwort

Sea plantain

Common scurvygrass

Thrift

Common rockrose

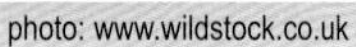

photo: www.wildstock.co.uk

Wild thyme

photo: www.wildstock.co.uk

Greater knapweed

Sea stacks and limestone cliffs, Marsden bay

photo: www.wildstock.co.uk

all plant photos: Dave Mitchell

Grass of Parnassus

Heather

Juniper

Hawthorn Dene, one of the numerous denes that dissect the coastline

photo: www.wildstock.co.uk

Occasional slippages on the slopes of the dene and adjacent cliffs create spaces into which smaller plants can germinate and survive. These include several species of orchids as well as tiny short-lived representatives of the gentian family such as Common Centaury (*Centaurium erythraea*), Autumn Gentian (*Gentianella amarella*) and Yellow-wort (*Blackstonia perfoliata*). In contrast, areas of cliff top adjacent to the dene are characterised by more acidic soils and support unusual coastal communities of Heather (*Calluna vulgaris*) and associated vegetation.

photo: Dave Mitchell

Common centaury

Unusual seepage flushes at Blackhall Rocks

The southernmost cliffs on the Durham Coast are characterised by peculiar armchair-shaped hollows, which receive calcium-rich seepage waters where glacial deposits meet the underlying Magnesian Limestone bedrock. At Blackhall Rocks, a very unusual assemblage of plants can be seen. For example, where the soils are thin and poor in nutrients, species usually associated with harsh upland habitats of the North-East occur, including Grass of Parnassus (*Parnassia palustris*), Bird's Eye Primrose (*Primula farinosa*), Round-Leaved Wintergreen (*Pyrola rotundifolia*) and Common Butterwort (*Pinguicula vulgaris*). The latter species is one of the few British plants that can capture and digest insects on its sticky leaves to provide extra nutrients in difficult growing conditions. Such plant assemblages are now rare and give us an idea of what the early vegetation of Britain must have been like after the ice melted at the end of the last ice age. It is living history.

photo: Dave Mitchell

Sea cliff hollow with rare vegetation, Blackhall Rocks

In contrast, where the soils are thicker and rich in nutrients, species usually associated with fen habitats of southern England occur here, including Blunt-Flowered Rush (*Juncus subnodulosus*), Fleabane (*Pulicaria dysenterica*), Hemp Agrimony (*Eupatorium cannabinum*)

photo: Dave Mitchell

Fleabane

and Greater Horsetail (*Equisetum telmateia*). Other species of interest include some of the last surviving bushes of Juniper (*Juniperus communis*) in lowland North East England as well as small populations of Brookweed (*Samolus valerandi*), normally associated with dune slacks.

Sand dunes
at Crimdon Dene

This represents the southernmost point on the Durham Coast and the only place on this coast where extensive sand dunes can be found.

On the beach in front of the dunes, a small pink-flowered representative of the cabbage family known as Sea Rocket (*Cakile maritima*) forms fragmented patches, surviving on decayed fragments of washed-up seaweeds. Its seeds can float around the coast in the sea and colonise sandy beaches like coconuts on tropical islands. Immediately behind these patches, an extensive system of mobile sand dunes has been built up by several drought-tolerant grasses, particularly Marram (*Ammophila arenaria*) and Lyme Grass (*Leymus arenarius*). Further inland, these give way to species-rich fixed dune vegetation where colourful plants such as Bloody Cranesbill (*Geranium sanguineum*), Spiny Restharrow (*Ononis spinosa*) and Lesser Meadow Rue (*Thalictrum minus*) grow in profusion. Of particular interest are plants of southern England, such as Burnt Orchid (*Orchis ustulata*) and Pyramidal Orchid (*Anacamptis pyramidalis*), which are at, or near, their northern limit. They grow alongside the rare Northern Purple Milk Vetch (*Astragalus danicus*), which is near its southern limit.

all plant photos: Dave Mitchell

Sea rocket

Pyramidal orchid

Bloody cranesbill

Burnt orchid

Purple milk vetch

Lyme grass

Dunes at Crimdon Dene

photo: www.wildstock.co.uk

Invertebrates of the Magnesian Limestone

by Terry Coult

photo: www.wildstock.co.uk
Burnet moth

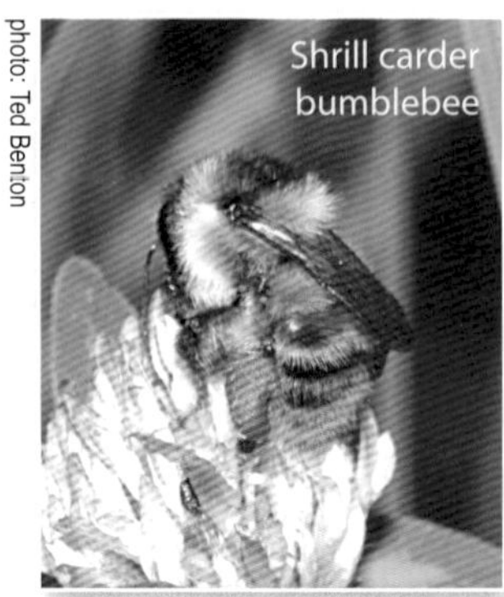
photo: Ted Benton
Shrill carder bumblebee

photo: www.wildstock.co.uk
Field grasshopper

The flower-rich grasslands of the Durham Magnesian Limestone, along with the coastal grasslands and denes, support a wealth of invertebrate life and are one of the most productive habitats in the whole of the county.

However, looks can be deceptive because, although the common invertebrates still abound, subtle but adverse changes in the environment have seen the long-term decline or loss of the specialists which are most sensitive to change.

Since it was first described in 1831, the "Durham" or "Castle Eden" Argus butterfly, now called the Northern Brown Argus, has been the most famous insect in Durham. Castle Eden Dene in the 19th century became the hunting ground of many entomologists seeking the "Durham Argus" and other butterflies, which once lived in and around the dene. Collectors came for butterflies such as Silver Washed Fritillary, Marsh Fritillary, Small Blue, Scotch Argus, Speckled Wood and Ringlet, all of which were lost to Durham more than a hundred years ago. The late 20th Century saw the return of the Speckled Wood and the Ringlet. Similarly, on the coast, the Gatekeeper and Grayling butterflies were 19th Century extinctions in Durham, which are only now beginning to make their way back into the county.

Another butterfly with changing fortunes, which can still be found on some of the Magnesian Limestone grasslands and along the coast, is the Dingy Skipper. In the first half of the 20th Century, it was on the increase but today it is under threat and colonies are becoming extinct across the county.

Common Rockrose is the food plant of the caterpillars of both the "Durham" Argus and the, brilliant metallic green day-flying moth the Cistus Forester. Historically recorded from Sherburn Hill and along the Durham coast, the Cistus Forester is still occasionally found on the coastal grasslands. Related to the Cistus Forester, but much more common and very easy to see, are the day-flying, Six Spot and Narrow Bordered Five Spot, Burnet moths, the latter introduced to Durham at Blackhall from Scarborough in 1891 by John R. Robson of Hartlepool, a famous local entomologist.

Castle Eden Dene was also a popular resort for moth collectors. In 1832, a new UK moth was found there; Captain

Blomer's Rivulet named after Captain Blomer who discovered it. Originally found only in Castle Eden Dene and then the nearby Hesleden Dene, the moth was thought to be unique to Durham. Since then, it has been found sparingly in other parts of the country and has become extinct in Hesleden Dene; Castle Eden Dene however, remains a stronghold.

Blomer's rivulet
photo: Charles Fletcher

The Magnesian Limestone has two other important, but threatened, endemic moths, the Least Minor and the Chalk Carpet, both are day flying and are rarely recorded.

Anyone searching for moths at night on the Magnesian Limestone grasslands might find their way lit by the light of the glowworm. Rarely found in Durham, its distribution on the coast has declined to only two known locations, Thrislington Plantation and Warren House Gill. Snails, the food of the glowworm, still abound on the Magnesian Limestone but even the snails are in decline with losses of specialist snails such as the Eccentric Grass Snail, the Moss Chrysalis Snail and the Heath Snail.

On a summer's day, the limestone grasslands are alive with the sight and sound of bumblebees, but again the

Glowworm
photo: Terry Coult

sensitive specialists like the Great Yellow Bumblebee and the Shrill Carder Bee have disappeared from Durham, in line with a national decline in bumblebees.

The coast and the Magnesian Limestone grassland support the two common grasshopper species, Common Green and Field Grasshopper, as well as the much less common Mottled Grasshopper. The Common Ground Hopper is very rare in the North-East but has in the past been found on the Magnesian Limestone and in Castle Eden Dene. The only cricket record for Durham is for the Grey Bush Cricket from Castle Eden Dene in 1833. As grassland diversity has declined, then so have the grasshoppers.

On a more positive note, the dragonflies of Durham are doing well, with an increase in the species to be found in the county. In recent years, the Ruddy Darter, Brown Hawker and Four Spotted Chaser have colonised the county, and species like the Black Darter and Southern Hawker have become much more abundant. All of the above can now be found on ponds across the Magnesian Limestone.

The Durham grasslands, coast and coastal denes have always been rich, happy, hunting grounds for entomologists and as the grasslands hum with insect life in the summer it's easy to believe that all is well. Taking a closer look however, shows just how much has been lost and how great the task is to restore first the flower rich grasslands and the limestone woodlands, and then the invertebrates that depend on them.

Cistus forester
photo: Keith Dover

Least minor
photo: Rob Petley Jones

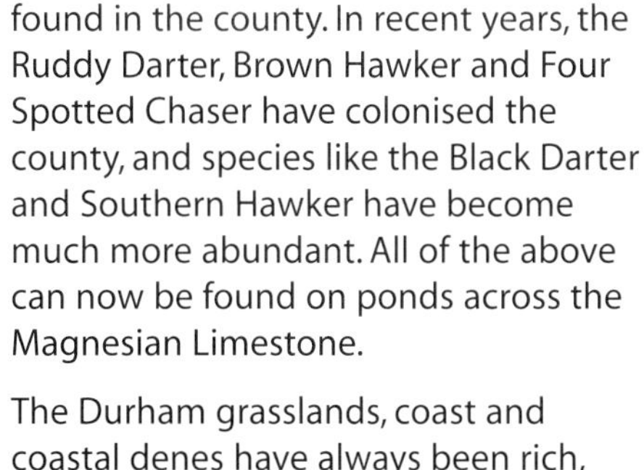
photo: www.wildstock.co.uk

Butterflies of the Magnesian Limestone

by Sam Ellis and Dave Wainwright

Marbled white

photo: www.wildstock.co.uk

Meadow brown

photo: www.wildstock.co.uk

Only 59 butterfly species are regularly recorded in the British Isles, many of which are confined to the warmer, southern counties of England. County Durham only sees just over half the British butterflies (32 since 1995), but nearly all these are encountered either regularly (20 species) or occasionally (8 species) in the Durham Magnesian Limestone Natural Area.

Flower-rich chalk and limestone grasslands produce the best habitat for butterflies. The Magnesian Limestone grasslands of Durham are no exception.

Foodplants for caterpillars and flowers for nectar are abundant. Sites on steep slopes and those with some scrub also provide the shelter loved by butterflies. Only one species, the Northern Brown Argus, a member of the blue family, is restricted to this habitat in Durham because the caterpillar foodplant, Common Rockrose (*Helianthemum nummularium*) is not found elsewhere.

Butterflies are what they eat, or at least what their caterpillars eat! The wide range of grasses present on Magnesian Limestone grassland support different butterflies, often in some abundance. The golden Small and Large Skippers both prefer quite tall grassland where their respective foodplants, Yorkshire Fog and Cock's-foot, grow. The other

Small copper

photo: www.wildstock.co.uk

Speckled wood

photo: www.wildstock.co.uk

grass feeders are all 'browns' with their distinctive eyespots, including the Meadow Brown, Ringlet, Small Heath and Wall. The Small Heath prefers fine-leaved grasses like the fescues whereas a sparse sward with bare ground is more important for the Wall. The Wall is a species in serious decline in southern England, but is still abundant here.

As well as the Northern Brown Argus, three other species feed on the leaves of flowers. Both the brightly coloured Common Blue and the unfortunately named Dingy Skipper feed on Common Bird's-foot-trefoil, but the latter only breeds in a short, sparse sward and is consequently scarcer. Also seen in small numbers is the beautiful Small Copper, whose caterpillars feed on sorrels.

Dingy skipper
photo: John Bridges

The other main groups present on the flower-rich grasslands are the 'whites' and 'vanessids'. The whites include Small, Large and Green-veined Whites and the aptly named Orange-tip. The vanessids include the familiar Red Admiral, Painted Lady, Small Tortoiseshell, Peacock and Comma, all of which you are just as likely to see nectaring on buddleias in the garden. These species are usually seen in small numbers, because their foodplants (e.g. Brassicas, nettles, thistles) are not abundant in this habitat.

Clouded yellow
photo: John Bridges

Comma
photo: www.wildstock.co.uk

Large Skipper
photo: John Bridges

Green-veined white
photo: John Bridges

Painted Lady
photo: John Bridges

Common Blue
(female)
photo: www.wildstock.co.uk
Common Blue
(male)
photo: John Bridges
Gatekeeper
photo: www.wildstock.co.uk
Orange Tip
photo: www.wildstock.co.uk
photo: John Bridges
Small tortoiseshell

Some butterflies are only seen very occasionally, including the two 'yellows', the Brimstone and the migrant Clouded Yellow. The rare Dark Green Fritillary has been recorded only a few times and the Marbled White is found at just one site, having been introduced as part of a scientific experiment on climate change to test whether or not Durham was now warm enough to support this butterfly.

In contrast to the grasslands, limestone woodlands support relatively few species. The occasional Holly Blue can be seen, but close inspection of canopy trees might reveal two of our more elusive butterflies, the Purple Hairstreak on oaks and the White-letter Hairstreak

photo: www.wildstock.co.uk

Holly blue

on elms. The latter is under threat from Dutch Elm Disease, but happily breeds on suckering elms, making it a bit more visible to the lepidopterist!

Butterflies are the fastest declining wildlife group in the country. In the past, when woods were more open, with bigger clearings and wider rides, more species were recorded but as woodland management changed in line with modern forestry practices butterfly numbers declined and some Durham species became extinct. Fortunately, several species have colonised or recolonised the region in recent decades, almost certainly due to a warming climate. These include the Small Skipper and the returning Ringlet and Comma in the late 1980s and 1990s, together with the Speckled Wood in the new millennium. Both the Grayling and the Gatekeeper have been seen again in the county and it is possible they might become re-established. Unfortunately the other extinct species are declining nationally and their nearest localities are too far away to have a realistic chance of recolonisation. Conservation efforts are now focused on ensuring the habitats of remaining scarce species like the Northern Brown Argus and Dingy Skipper are not lost.

Northern Brown Argus butterfly

The Northern Brown Argus butterfly is one of only five resident British species with a northern distribution, with populations in both Scotland and northern England. This butterfly is restricted to four distinct areas in northern England, with the Durham Magnesian Limestone Natural Area the south-eastern edge of its British range. Until recent genetic studies clarified the position, the northern England populations were often referred to as a separate subspecies, the Durham or Castle Eden Argus.

The Northern Brown Argus is a member of the 'blue' family, but unlike all but the closely related Brown Argus, neither the male nor female has any blue on the upperwings. They are sometimes confused with female Common Blues, which have some blue at the base of

photo: www.wildstock.co.uk

Northern brown argus

the forewings but the Northern Brown Argus is smaller and has a characteristic silvery appearance when in flight caused by the reflection of light on the underwings. In Scotland the butterfly has a distinctive white spot in the centre of the forewing, a feature normally absent or scarce in northern England, although it is present in about 5% of individuals on the Durham coast.

The butterfly flies in June, July and into August, occurring on both inland and coastal sites. This is a sedentary butterfly with most adults flying together in clearly defined colonies. On the coast it can be recorded from north of Seaham to north of Hartlepool, with 23 colonies. The 11 inland colonies are nearly all located on the western edge of the escarpment between High Pittington and Bishop Middleham. More than half the sites are small, supporting less than 0.1ha of suitable habitat, where the populations are less than 100 adults. Conversely, Thrislington NNR has over 10ha of habitat and supports a population of up to 2000 adults.

With the exception of a single sand dune site, the butterfly is restricted to

COMMON NAME	SCIENTIFIC NAME	STATUS
Small Skipper	Thymelicus sylvestris Poda	Regularly recorded
Large Skipper	Ochlodes sylvanus Esper	Regularly recorded
Dingy Skipper	Erynnis tages L.	Regularly recorded
Clouded Yellow	Colius croceus Geoffrey	Occasional
Brimstone	Gonepteryx rhamni L.	Occasional
Large White	Pieris brassicae L.	Regularly recorded
Small White	Pieris rapae L.	Regularly recorded
Green-veined White	Pieris napi L.	Regularly recorded
Orange-tip	Anthocharis cardamines L.	Regularly recorded
Green Hairstreak	Callophrys rubi L.	Occasional
Purple Hairstreak	Neozephyrus quercus L.	Occasional
White-letter Hairstreak	Satyrium w-album Knoch	Regularly recorded
Small Copper	Lycaena phlaeas L.	Regularly recorded
Northern Brown Argus	Plebeius artaxerxes Fabricius	Regularly recorded
Common Blue	Polyommatus icarus Rott.	Regularly recorded
Holly Blue	Celastrina argiolus L.	Occasional
Red Admiral	Vanessa atalanta L.	Regularly recorded
Painted Lady	Cynthia cardui L.	Regularly recorded
Small Tortoiseshell	Aglais urticae L.	Regularly recorded
Peacock	Inachis io L.	Regularly recorded
Comma	Polygonia c-album L.	Regularly recorded
Dark Green Fritillary	Argynnis aglaja L.	Occasional
Speckled Wood	Pararge aegeria L.	Occasional
Wall	Lasiommata megera L.	Regularly recorded
Marbled White	Melanargia galathea L.	Occasional
Meadow Brown	Maniola jurtina L.	Regularly recorded
Ringlet	Aphantopus hyperantus L.	Regularly recorded
Small Heath	Coenonympha pamphilus L.	Regularly recorded

Magnesian Limestone grasslands in Durham. The common feature of all sites is the presence of the caterpillar foodplant, Common Rockrose (*Helianthemum nummularium*) growing in a lightly grazed or ungrazed sward. The distinctive white eggs are laid on the upper leaf surface and larger thicker leaves towards the shoot tip are preferred. Like other 'blue' butterflies, the caterpillars produce a sugary secretion attractive to ants. Caterpillars are protected by ants from attack or infection in exchange for the sweet secretion, though this has been observed only infrequently.

There have been eleven recorded extinctions since the early 1980s, all but one on small sites. Losses are usually attributable to either overgrazing or agricultural abandonment leading to scrub invasion. During the 1990s conservation effort focused on scrub removal and the introduction of light grazing regimes appears to have halted the decline. At the landscape scale, it is no coincidence that all extinctions have occurred on inland sites which are more fragmented and isolated than coastal colonies, making recolonisation much less likely. The effect of climate change is an unknown quantity but it may be that global warming may make some Durham sites unsuitable for this species.

The Dingy Skipper

The Dingy Skipper is a drab grey and brown butterfly that looks very much like a moth. It is on the wing during May and June and is often seen making rapid flights close to the ground, preferring to bask on bare ground or stones and occasionally feeding on various flowers.

Dingy skipper

photo: www.wildstock.co.uk

County Durham is an important region for the butterfly. More than 80 inland sites support it and it is also widespread along the coast between Hartlepool and Seaham.

The butterfly requires a combination of bare ground interspersed with taller vegetation. The main caterpillar foodplant is Common Bird's-foot-trefoil, although Greater Bird's-foot-trefoil and Horseshoe Vetch are occasionally used. These requirements restrict the butterfly to two main habitat types within County Durham: brownfield sites and Magnesian Limestone grassland. The number of inland colonies has declined by around a third since 1990 and most of these losses have arisen through redevelopment of brownfield sites, with few if any of the colonies on Magnesian Limestone grassland having gone extinct. Continued protection and enhancement of this important habitat is crucial if the butterfly's future within the county is to be ensured.

TEN BEST BUTTERFLY SITES

1. Thrislington Plantation NNR: This site supports one of the largest Northern Brown Argus populations in northern England. The population has steadily increased since 1990. Several large exclosures, where grazing is light, help maintain suitable habitat for the butterfly. Dingy Skippers are present although rarely in high numbers and White-letter Hairstreak can also be found here, breeding on elm trees.

2. Bishop Middleham Quarry. This site supports large populations of both Northern Brown Argus and Dingy Skipper. The warm microclimate means the quarry usually has the earliest records of the year. The vegetation grows slowly on the thin soil so the habitat remains good for butterflies for many years.

3. Cassop Vale NNR. A small Northern Brown Argus population occurs here and Dingy Skippers are occasionally reported, usually in ones or twos. Light grazing by cattle and sheep help maintain suitable conditions for the butterflies.

4. Little Wood LNR. This site supports a large Dingy Skipper colony and a small Northern Brown Argus population is also present. Recent habitat creation works are likely to increase the abundance of both in future years.

5. Wingate Quarry LNR: Dingy Skipper numbers seem to be rising at this site, possibly in response to increased Common Bird's-foot-trefoil abundance. The Marbled White occurs here well to the north of its natural range, which extends only to the Yorkshire Wolds. The butterfly was released as part of a scientific experiment into the impact of climate change. Although a population has become established, the Marbled White has not yet colonised other nearby sites.

6. Blackhall Rocks: This site supports the largest area of Common Rock-rose on the coast centred on Blue House Gill and is therefore a key site for Northern Brown Argus. Dingy Skippers can be found wherever Common Bird's-foot-trefoil grows, sometimes in high numbers.

7. Castle Eden Dene NNR: The Northern Brown Argus was first described from the Castle Eden Dene coast, hence the early name of Castle Eden Argus. Two coastal colonies are still present, but the small population at the western end of the dene became extinct again in the late 1990s despite a reintroduction attempt. Dingy Skippers occur here in good numbers and White-letter Hairstreak butterflies can also be found breeding on elm trees.

8. Warren House Gill: Another good coastal site supporting populations of both Northern Brown Argus and Dingy Skipper. Suitable habitat occurs in both the gill and on the seaward cliffs.

9. Tunstall Hills LNR. Dingy Skippers are present in fairly good numbers. Main colonies are located within the disused quarry and around Maiden Paps.

10. Marsden Old Quarry. Dingy Skippers have not been seen at this site as yet, although recent habitat creation work by South Tyneside Council has improved habitat condition and the butterfly is likely to colonise in due course.

Mammals, Reptiles and Amphibians of the Durham Magnesian Limestone

by Terry Coult

photo: www.wildstock.co.uk

photo www.wildstock.co.uk

Mammals

The dramatic changes undergone by the area's mammals was illustrated by an incident in 1878. Quarrymen working the limestone of the Cleadon Hills, near Whitburn Lizards, uncovered a cave in which were found human bones along with numerous gnawed bones of native mammals and birds, including the remains of the now extinct flightless seabird the Great Auk. Wild mammal bones found in the cave were Wild Boar, Red and Roe deer, Fox, Badger, Pine Marten, Weasel, Hedgehog, Mole and abundant Water Vole bones; no doubt the remains of various carnivorous feasts. By the time the cave was quarried in 1878, the Wild Boar was extinct in Britain, the Pine Marten confined to the wilds of Scotland and the Badger, Red and Roe deer almost extinct in the North-East.

Red deer became extinct in the wild in Durham, probably, during the 17th Century and now exist in the county only in a private park. By the early 18th Century, the Roe was gone from the east of Durham, mainly due to deforestation, but lingered in very small numbers in the west of the county and on the Northumberland border. Today, it has spread back to its former haunts, recolonising the larger coastal denes during the 1960s.

By the end of the 19th Century, the unrelenting massacre of carnivores by gamekeepers caused the demise in Durham of the Pine Marten, the Wild Cat, and Polecat, one of the last of which was reported by the Rev. G. C. Abbes, of Cleadon, in his garden. The Wild Cat became confined to the far north and west of Scotland and the Polecat to Wales.

In 1895, Sir Alfred Pease, the badger-digging MP for Cleveland, wrote that the Badger was extinct in Durham. Whether this was true is uncertain, but it was certainly the nadir in the fortunes of the Badger in Durham; since that date the Badger has expanded in both numbers and range and can once again be found in the woods and denes of the east of the county. That other large carnivore the Otter seems to have survived the depredations of the gamekeeper, hanging on in the county until almost completely disappearing during the England otter population crash of the 1950s and 60s, which was caused by pesticide pollution in rivers and streams.

Today, the Otter is recolonising the rivers and streams of County Durham, even as far as the City of Sunderland and into the urban conurbations of Stockton and Middlesborough. Whether it ever permanently occupies the denes and coast of east Durham remains to be seen, but there have been a handful of recent tenuous otter records on the Durham coast.

The most ubiquitous large carnivore of them all, the Fox, made it all the way through despite intensive persecution, the reason almost certainly being that after the crash in deer numbers it was promoted to a beast of the chase and was preserved on some sporting estates so that it could be pursued by hounds, a paradox of the hunting psyche. The smaller carnivores Stoat and Weasel are still present across the whole of the county.

Water Vole bones were found by the quarrymen in 1878 as well, which may have much to do with the local geography. The River Don flows into the Tyne at Jarrow and its extensive tributary system drains the flatlands of South Tyneside, bordered to the east by the Magnesian Limestone escarpment at Cleadon Hills. It is quite likely that the Water Vole bones found in the Whitburn cave were the remains of meals caught by predators in the streams and ditches

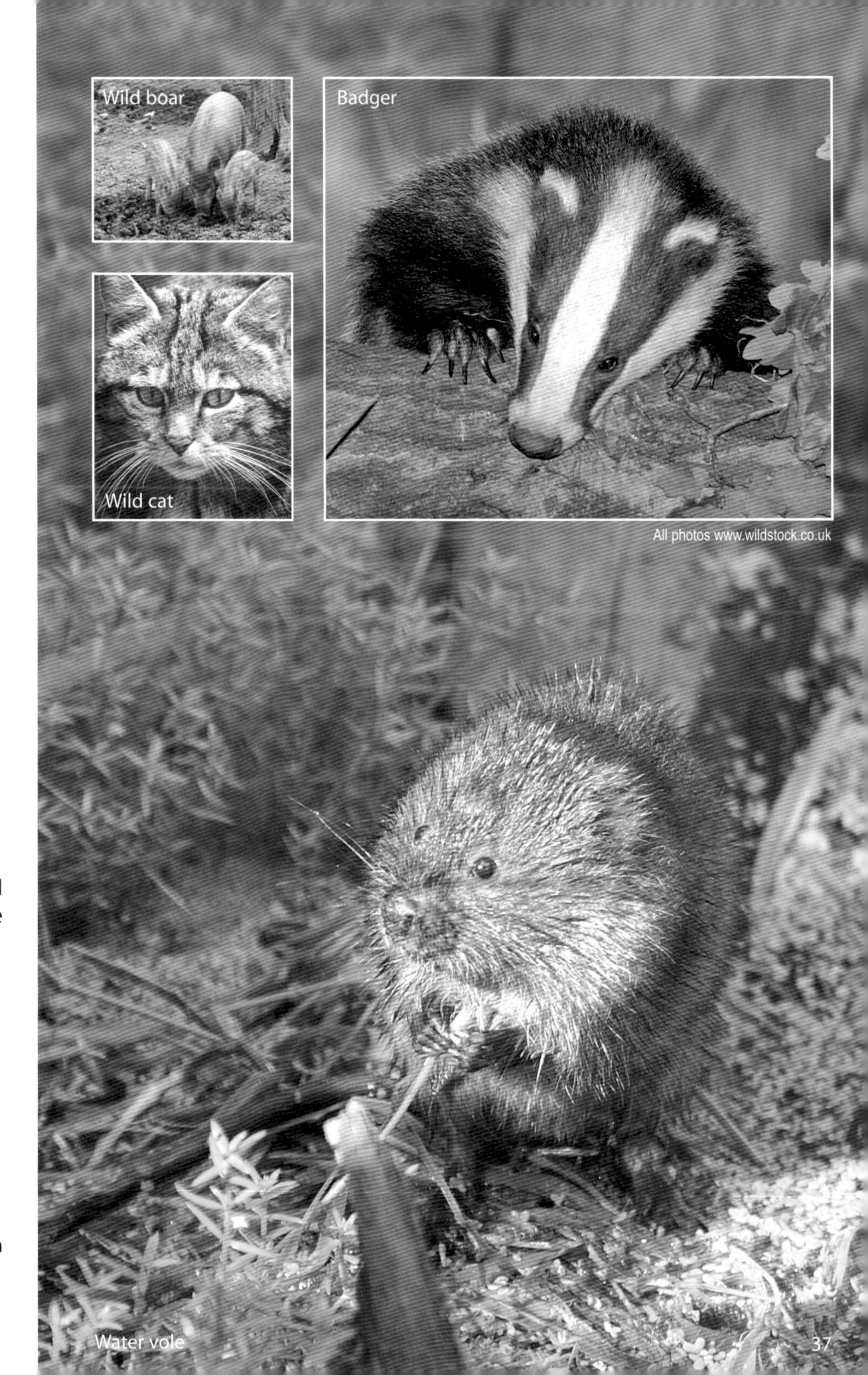

Wild boar

Badger

Wild cat

All photos www.wildstock.co.uk

Water vole

All photos www.wildstock.co.uk

which feed the Don. Once common on all streams and rivers in the North-East, the Water Vole has suffered a massive population crash across the UK and is threatened with national extinction. The Don and its tributaries however, still remain a home to the Water Vole, but for how long?

Of the smaller mammals, the Bank and Field Vole along with the Woodmouse are ubiquitous across the region but the Harvest Mouse is rarely recorded. The only Magnesian Limestone record is a possible from Hawthorn Dene in 1975. Distribution of the shrews is not well known, although it is likely that Common and Pygmy Shrew are ubiquitous. Water Shrew has been recorded from Hawthorn Dene and a few other scattered localities across the county. The other insectivores the Hedgehog and Mole remain widespread in the county.

Bat records for east Durham include, Noctule, Pipistrelle, Brown Long Eared and Daubenton's.

Common Seals still breed on Seal Sands at Teesmouth and both they and Grey Seals can be seen off the coast and in the river estuaries.

The most recent native mammal to be lost from the east of Durham is the Red Squirrel, still present in a few places across the county including some of the coastal denes. Up to the turn of the 21st Century, the red squirrel had been almost completely replaced in Durham by the introduced American grey squirrel, which is now widespread in the county.

Like the Grey Squirrel, many mammals found in Durham are aliens, which arrived by hitching a lift on ships or were deliberately introduced. The Brown Rat reached the UK in the 18th Century, eventually displacing the Black or Ship Rat, which had been here much longer. Mostly associated with the coast, the Black Rat disappeared from North-East ports during the latter half of the 20th Century. For example, six Black Rats were killed on ships in Hartlepool docks in 1965, whereas in 1928 the number was 1,771. No doubt black rats continue to occasionally arrive on board ship but are unable to colonise our ports and harbours. The Brown Rat is now widespread and common in Durham. Similarly the ubiquitous House Mouse is an alien, dependent on man to transport it around the world.

It is thought that the Normans introduced Fallow Deer and Rabbits to the UK as food; the latter were kept in specially constructed enclosures called warrens, the word often appearing in place names, as at Hart Warren. In the 19th Century, there were a number of deer parks around the county, including one at Wynyard with Fallow Deer. Today, Fallow Deer are only found in two parks in central Durham. Similarly the brown hare, which displaced the native Mountain Hare over most of the UK, was introduced, possibly in the Iron Age for food and for sport.

The most recent coloniser is the American Mink; escaping from fur farms during the mid 20th Century the Mink had now colonised most of the UK mainland, including the rivers and streams of east Durham. The first reports appeared on the River Wear in 1977.

The immediate future is likely to herald another change in the form of Chinese Muntjac, a tiny deer introduced into southern Britain which have recently spread north across the Tees and are colonising parts of Durham.

Amphibians and reptiles

The Tyne to Tees coast has no credible recent records of snakes but the legless, snake-like lizard the Slowworm is occasionally recorded from the coastal denes. The Common Lizard has been recorded along the coast, including most of the denes, Blackhall Rocks and Hart Warren. Common Frog, Common Toad, Smooth, Palmate and Great Crested Newt are all present in ponds on the Magnesian Limestone. The Palmate Newt however, is very scarce, being more a newt of the western uplands.

Common toad

All photos www.wildstock.co.uk

Grey seal

Stoat

Field vole

Bank vole

Brown hare

Great crested newt

Slowworm

The Birds of the Durham Magnesian Limestone

by John Olley

Ringed plover

Stonechat

When it comes to birdlife, the area supports one of the richest diversity of species in Britain. The reason is that it offers many habitats, everything from the open sea, cliffs, coastal grassland and denes to inland farmland, woodland, hedgerows, wetlands and valley streams. Some of Britain's most important species are to be found across the area. But even though some are scarce, whatever time of year you wander this area there is always something of interest to see.

All photos: www.wildstock.co.uk

Short-eared owl

That birds have survived and thrived on the coast is down, in part, to the dramatic improvements in habitats over recent years. For years, the Durham coast was blighted by coal spoil deposits but today, after the success of the Turning the Tide clean-up project, a huge change is occurring, making it more attractive to birds. One of the features is the return, coming in from the open sea during winter and spring, of large populations of Common Scoter, Red Breasted Merganser, Eider, Red Throated Diver and various terns. There is always a chance of a rarity over the sea, including Black Throated, Great Northern Divers, Storm Petrel and Leaches Storm Petrel, Shearwaters, Gannet, Long Tailed Duck and Skuas. Patience is certainly well rewarded on the Durham coast.

The cleaned-up shoreline and beaches are also busy with waders scurrying for food and setting up nesting territories, including Oystercatcher and Ringed Plover, which now regularly breed, and Redshank, Knot, Sanderling and Turnstone all returning for the autumn and wintering in increasing numbers.

Limestone cliffs form prominent features along the coast and provide nesting and foraging areas at all times of the year for a variety of species. Look

Redshank

All photos: www.wildstock.co.uk

closely and you will see Cormorant, Fulmar, Kittiwake, Gulls, Jackdaws and Rock Pipit.

Also good for birds are the coastal grassland, scrub and farmland areas, supporting large populations of Skylark, Meadow Pipit, Reed Bunting, Yellowhammer, Stonechat and Short Eared Owls, which abound over the cliff and scrub interface.

Kittiwake

Skylark

Heron

Bullfinch

Greater-spotted woodpecker

Merlin

Yellowhammer

Waxwing

© Allan Jones

Willow warbler

Photo: Allan Jones

All photos (unless credited): www.wildstock.co.uk

Sparrowhawk

The coastal area is also very important in providing a refuge for global travellers and sometimes you can see large movements of common and rare passage birds in spring and autumn. Among species which can gather in large numbers are Redwings, Fieldfares, finches and geese, moving inland during the autumn. You can also enjoy the sight of Great Grey Shrike, Icterine, Barred, and the tiny Pallas's and Yellow Browed Warblers.

Birds of prey do not miss out either and Honey Buzzard, Hen Harrier and Montagues Harriers are rare spring visitors as they return to their upland and continental breeding grounds.

Because the coastal denes are valuable remnants of once-larger blocks of woodland, they are very important for common woodland birds such as the finches and titmice. Bullfinches are found in scrubby areas with Greenfinch, Chaffinch and Goldfinch being common. Also adding colour are Blue,

Tree sparrow

Nuthatch

All photos (unless credited): www.wildstock.co.uk

Great, Willow and Marsh tits. Warblers such as Common Whitethroat , Blackcap, Chiffchaff and Willow Warbler all have high populations.

The Green and Greater Spotted Woodpecker are very much at home here with the acrobatic Nuthatch and Treecreeper in the more mature sites.

Also, Buzzards are becoming a regular species over the denes with Merlin in the winter and Sparrowhawk and Kestrel regularly breeding.

As we move inland to the more open farmed areas, we see a change; here the main land use emphasis is on food production so farmland birds tend to dominate. Important populations of species such as Grey and Red legged Partridges, Corn Bunting and Tree Sparrow are found here. Some areas still hold small populations of Lapwing and Curlew and important wetland sites are to found at Bishop Middleham and Hurworth Burn reservoir with smaller ponds near Trimdon Village. The Bishop Middleham complex has developed through minewater subsidence and these wetlands are of local significance, supporting large flocks of wildfowl including Wigeon, Teal, Shoveler, Gadwall and Mallard in their hundreds. And waders such as Golden Plover, Lapwing and Redshank can be impressive as well.

Breeding populations of birds in the area are high with Yellow Wagtail, Little Ringed Plover and grebes doing well. Old and working quarries provide refuges for Sand Martins, the declining Tree Pipit, Yellowhammer and various warblers.

In 2002, though, a very different visitor arrived in the form of a pair of Bee-Eaters, which were well off their normal breeding area and took up residence at Bishop Middleham Quarry, the first UK breeding for more than 50 years.

Lapwing

Grey partridge

Photo: Richard Dunn

Bee-eaters

Kestrel

The Future

by Julie Stobbs and Michelle Appleby

This publication describes the unique nature of Durham's Magnesian Limestone, charting its history from the geological legacy of the Zechstein Sea to the effects of human influences on the landscape and the wildlife it supports. The effects have included harvesting crops from the surface of the ground and exploiting the mineral wealth below. Despite this long history of use of the resource, there remains a unique historic and wildlife legacy that can be found nowhere else in the UK.

From the second half of the 20th Century onwards concern for the natural environment and its conservation has grown apace and, as public awareness of the natural environment has increased, it might be assumed that the worst is over and that there is cause for optimism. The 21st Century brings its own new threats, however.

Like many other habitats that are important in nature conservation terms, Magnesian Limestone grassland now has a highly fragmented distribution. This isolation makes it vulnerable to many pressures that can lead to its piecemeal loss. Over the past two hundred years the most significant amongst these threats has been agricultural intensification. Ploughing and reseeding of unimproved grassland, conversion of pasture to arable land and increased use of fertilisers and herbicides have all had a negative impact on the grasslands and wildlife of the Magnesian Limestone.

photo: www.wildstock.co.uk

Intensively managed farm landscape

In many cases a reduction in biodiversity (the overall wildlife, both plant and animal that the area supports) can be linked to what nature conservationists would call inappropriate management. Applications of fertiliser, over-grazing, or equally, neglect and an absence of grazing can dramatically change the wildlife value of grasslands but, as the agricultural sector has historically adapted to changing markets and government policies, the intrinsic value of wildlife has rarely been top of the farm agenda.

An absence of grazing can soon lead to encroachment with coarse grass species and the development of scrub, both of which out-compete the more delicate grasses and broad-leaved species which make up the traditional and highly

photo: Ian Armstrong

Highland cattle are sometimes used for conservation grazing

attractive Magnesian Limestone grasslands. Old accounts show that many areas that are now un-grazed, such as the grasslands along the Durham Coast, were in the past grazed, and formerly supported more diverse and abundant plant and invertebrate communities.

All is not lost, however. In recent years there has been a significant shift in agricultural subsidies with the emphasis moving from maximising production to sustainable management of land. This new approach is a direct recognition of the biodiversity value of our landscape, and the importance of the Magnesian Limestone grassland to the overall biodiversity of the UK. Agri-environment schemes administered by Natural England specifically target Magnesian Limestone grasslands, making funding

Hebridean sheep at Crow Trees Local Nature Reserve

photo: Ian Armstrong

available to manage sites appropriately for their conservation value. The opportunity now exists to re-introduce grazing on areas like the Durham coast, using traditional breeds such as belted Galloway cattle and Hebridean sheep, which are suited to less intensive agricultural practices.

New conflicts can still occur, of course. New quarrying, development of

Juniper

photo: lDave Mitchell

previously-used land, "brownfield" in developers' language, and the growth in recreational use of the countryside all bring their unique and sometimes cumulative pressures. Brownfield development is the Government's attempt to take pressure away from greenfield sites but, where brownfield has lain undisturbed for many years, it often has more value for wildlife than the surrounding intensively farmed landscape.

Although many sites now enjoy nature conservation designations, as explained in the chapter on "Current Status", there is nevertheless always a threat from road construction, housing and other built developments and the need for targeted and effective nature conservation continues.

Increasingly now, the native flora and fauna of Magnesian Limestone grassland can be affected by warming climate. This is particularly significant for some of the 'northern' elements of these unique communities like Bird's Eye Primrose, Grass of Parnassus and Juniper, which were hitherto more widespread on the Magnesian Limestone, particularly on the coast, but are less likely to be able to tolerate the consistently warmer temperatures now predicted.

In contrast, some species of southern affinity may now be becoming more widespread in their distribution. This certainly seems to be the case for Upright Brome which is becoming more common and is even somewhat of a problem at several Magnesian Limestone grassland sites including Thrislington National Nature Reserve. There are similar parallels with

Southern hawker

invertebrate species; for instance dragonflies such as the Southern Hawker have been extending their ranges northwards for several years, now that warmer summers are becoming the norm.

Global warming poses many questions for nature conservation. If the environment is changing to such an

photo: Dave Mitchell

Grass of Parnassus

extent that the plants and animals that once thrived are no longer able to tolerate the warmth, then what can be done and is it our place to attempt it? Perhaps nature should be left to take its course, but can it really do so in a landscape so markedly changed by human activities? How can the plants and animals of fragmented habitats move through a landscape where the distance to a suitable site for occupancy can be many kilometres? Recent conservation initiatives are increasingly looking to landscape-scale projects which allow these movements to take place by creating habitat links.

Protecting and Enhancing the Resource

With the appropriate will, knowledge and resources, important sites can be *conserved*, formerly important sites can either be *restored* or *enhanced* and, perhaps most importantly, through appropriate spatial planning, important habitats can be *linked*. Perhaps in the future land use planners, rather than nature conservationists, will have the greatest role to play in conserving the unique character of the Magnesian Limestone areas of County Durham. Combining "habitat creation", which is used to develop new habitats in suitable areas, with the concept of "connectivity" may well be the tool which allows these two groups to work together. A modern and integrated approach to land management relies greatly on a strategy that will often allow plants and animals to move through the landscape.

MAGical Meadows survey work

As humankind seeks to adapt to changing environmental conditions it is vital that we continue to record our native flora and fauna and to monitor any changes in their relative abundance which may be taking place. In order for this work to be undertaken properly by trained individuals it is essential that the necessary funding is found for surveys, monitoring and research, which will inform future land management decisions.

On a positive note, it is appropriate to highlight the work of some of the many excellent partnerships that are doing so much to ensure that the unique interest of the Magnesian Limestone Natural Area is appropriately conserved and managed. Notable amongst these are:

- the MAGical Meadows Project lead by Durham Wildlife Trust, funded by the Aggregates Levy Sustainability Fund, under whose auspices this booklet has been produced;
- the Durham Biodiversity Partnership, which has identified a variety of targets and implemented actions for key species and habitats within the Durham area including Magnesian Limestone Grassland;
- the Durham Heritage Coast Partnership, which has continued much of the good work originally set up by the Millennium Commission-funded Turning the Tide project;
- the Grazing Animals Project, which works to promote links between land owners and managers with the owners of grazing animals to ensure that grazing regimes are developed which are most advantageous for nature conservation.

There is now a growing awareness of the importance and interest of the North East's Magnesian Limestone grassland, promoted in part through the interpretative and educational work carried out by organisations such as Natural England, Durham Wildlife Trust and the various local authorities. It is hoped that this publication will go some way to further raising the profile of this habitat type.

Predicting the future is impossible but, with good planning and the will to grasp new opportunities when they arise, it will be possible to harness the energy of all sectors of the community to achieve a common conservation aim. Working with groups such as planners, farmers, quarry companies, highway officers, schools and colleges, together with local interest and community groups, many opportunities will exist to help benefit the biodiversity interest of this important habitat. Striving to achieve our conservation goals requires a flexible, pragmatic and often opportunistic approach.

Common Blue (male) photo: www.wildstock.co.uk

Hoary plantain photo: www.wildstock.co.uk

Frog orchid photo: Dave Mitchell

Upright brome photo: Dave Mitchell

Silver-y moth photo: www.wildstock.co.uk

Rockrose on limestone photo: www.wildstock.co.uk

Ten Places to Visit

photo: www.wildstock.co.uk

Publicly accessible places to visit, offering a chance to get to know the Magnesian Limestone flora and fauna, are well distributed between the Tyne and the Tees. Below are ten sites where access on foot is unrestricted and it is possible to learn about and enjoy the unique habitats and species of the Magnesian Limestone as well as important geological features.

Thrislington Plantation

National Nature Reserve

Description

Thrislington Plantation supports the largest stand of primary Magnesian Limestone grassland in Britain, having survived attempted afforestation in Victorian times, scrub encroachment after grazing animals were removed from the site in the 1950s and a proposed quarry extension in the1980s.

The site has been rated the UK's best example of Magnesian Limestone grassland and further designated as a Special Area of Conservation. Visit the site between May and August to see the Magnesian Limestone grassland in full bloom. Thrislington supports the full range of Magnesian Limestone grassland species and the nationally scarce plants Perennial Flax, Blue Moor-Grass and Dark Red Helleborine.

The site also has a wealth of invertebrates including Northern Brown Argus Butterfly, Dingy Skipper Butterfly, Least Minor Moth, and Glowworm.

Location

Entrance to the reserve is via a public footpath leading off the minor road between West Cornforth and Ferryhill Station. Parking is in the lay by adjacent to the reserve sign, one mile south of West Cornforth and opposite the Thrislington works, at grid reference NZ309325.

General Information

Grid Ref: NZ316325
OS Explorer Map No. 305

photo: www.wildstock.co.uk

Wingate Quarry

Managed by Natural England full details of the site can be found on the NE website.

Wingate Quarry

Local Nature Reserve

Description

A limestone quarry abandoned in the 1930s, the site is now important for its exposures of limestone, secondary limestone grassland, neutral grasslands with associated flora along with scrub, woodland and wetland. Invertebrates include Marbled White Butterfly and Chalk Carpet Moth.

Location

Off the B1278 minor road between Old Thornley and Trimdon Colliery, parking is at the reserve entrance.

General Information

Grid Ref: NZ371374
OS Explorer map no. 305

Managed by Durham County Council. Full details of the site are available from DCC and from the DCC website.

Location map showing ten sites that you can visit

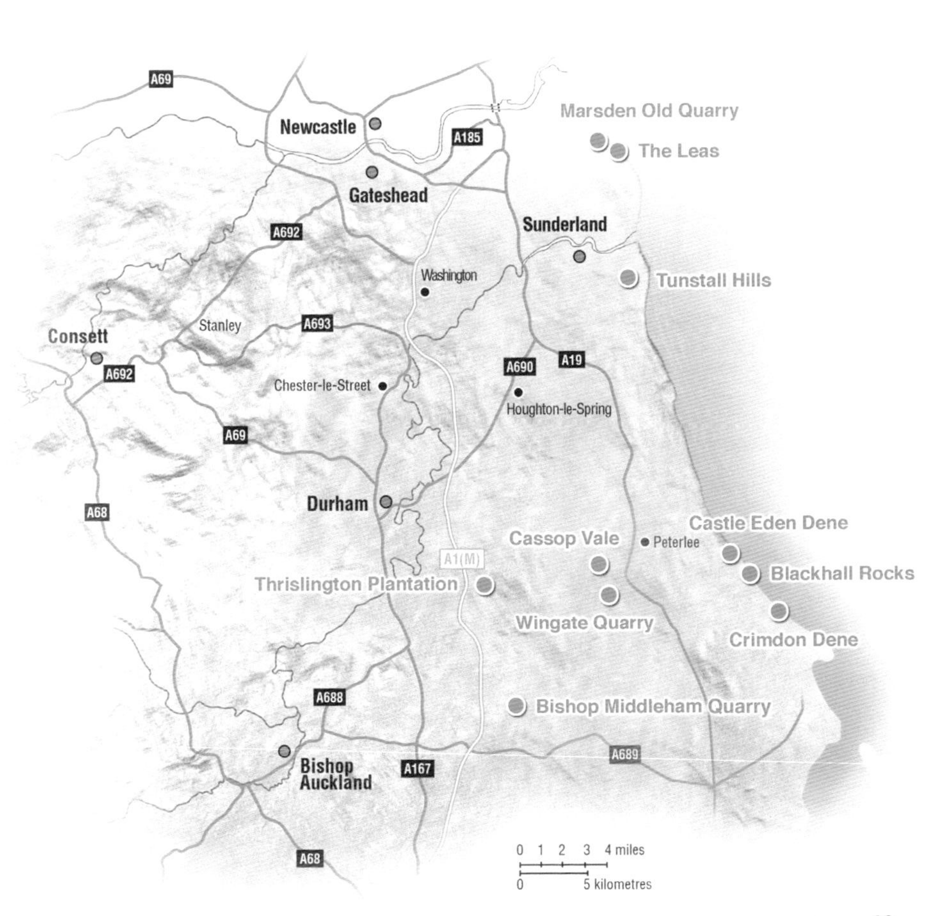

Marsden Old Quarry

Marsden Old Quarry

Local Nature Reserve

Description

A small site with excellent exposures of concretionary limestone and a range of limestone grassland types including areas dominated by Blue Moor Grass. Small Scabious, Common Rockrose, Carline Thistle, Fairy Flax and Autumn Gentian are also present. The quarry is a renowned location for migrant birds in the autumn with a regular show of common migrants and the occasional rarity.

photo: www.wildstock.co.uk

Marsden Old Quarry

Marsden Old Quarry

photo: www.wildstock.co.uk

Location

Parking and access at the north end of Lizard Lane in Marsden opposite the caravan park.

General Information

Grid Ref: NZ395645
OS Explorer map no. 316

Managed by South Tyneside Council. Full details are available on the South Tyneside Council website.

Bishop Middleham Quarry

Durham Wildlife Trust Nature Reserve

Description

A limestone quarry abandoned in the 1930s and since that time colonised by a variety of limestone flora, producing a secondary Magnesian Limestone grassland. This rare habitat supports a range of orchids such as Pyramidal, Common Spotted, Bee and Fragrant orchid and most importantly a large number of Dark Red Helleborines. The sparse grassland of the quarry floor also supports Blue Moor Grass, Moonwort, Autumn Gentian and Fairy Flax along with extensive areas of Common Rockrose, the

photo: www.wildstock.co.uk

Bishop Middleham Quarry

photo: www.wildstock.co.uk

latter being the food plant of the caterpillar of the Northern Brown Argus butterfly which can also be found in the quarry.

The site is best seen between April and July for the orchids, June and July for Northern Brown Argus butterfly and July, for Dark Red Helleborine.

Location
Situated half a mile north of the village of Bishop Middleham on a minor road linking Bishop Middleham to the A177. Car parking is restricted to two lay-bys on the west side of the road.

General information
Grid Ref: NZ331326.
OS Explorer Map No. 305

Managed by Durham Wildlife Trust. Details of the site can be found on the DWT website.

Bishop Middleham Quarry

photo: www.wildstock.co.uk

Blackhall Rocks

National Nature Reserve, Durham Wildlife Trust Nature Reserve

Description
A natural exposure of reef limestone, topped by boulder clay with a total cliff height of 60 feet, the southern end of the site has the largest caves on the Durham coast.

The cliffs support an internationally unique grassland community with a very rich flora including Quaking Grass, Common Rockrose, Salad Burnet and Bloody Cranesbill. The wet gullies contain rare plants such as Butterwort, Round Leaved Wintergreen, Grass of Parnassus, Brookweed and Birds Eye Primrose. The locally rare fern Sea Spleenwort grows on the cliffs.

Northern Brown Argus butterfly and Cistus Forester moths can be found on the cliff slopes.

The beaches at Blackhall suffered from a century of dumping of colliery spoil from the undersea deep coal mines of the Durham coast. Since dumping ceased the natural currents of the coast

Blackhall meadow

have begun the process of gradually moving the pit waste.

Location
East of Blackhall Colliery. From the crossroads on the A1086 at Blackhall Rocks village, follow the minor road under the railway bridge and down towards the beach. There is a large car park on the right of the road or taking the left hand fork leads to a very small car park just above the cliff tops.

General information
Grid Ref: NZ470392
OS Explorer Map No. 308

photo: www.wildstock.co.uk

Managed by Durham Wildlife Trust full details of the site can be found on the DWT website.

Common Rockrose

photo: www.wildstock.co.uk

The Leas

Description
A large cliff top site showing classic examples of coastal erosion including stacks, arches and wave cut platforms. It is the largest area of semi-natural grassland in South Tyneside ranging from neutral to limestone.
A particularly rich area known as Rocket Green (opposite the old limekilns) holds many typical Magnesian Limestone grassland species plus rarer wild flowers like Bee and Pyramidal Orchid, Yellow-Wort, Saw-Wort and Dropwort.

The Leas

photo: www.wildstock.co.uk

Blackhall Rocks

Location
Access and car parking are off the Coast Road between South Shields and Souter Lighthouse.

General Information
OS Grid Ref: NZ395657
OS Explorer map no. 316

Managed by the National Trust. Further information is available from the National Trust website.

Crimdon Dene

Description
Crimdon Dene contains a variety of special habitats ranging from the ancient semi-natural woodlands in the Dene to the sand dunes and paramaritime Magnesian Limestone grasslands found on the coastal slopes.

The Dene itself is a wide valley cut through boulder clay into the Magnesian Limestone and the overlying boulder clay drift deposit. Both layers can be seen in the stream bed near the railway viaduct where the Magnesian Limestone is exposed. The wooded sides are an example of ancient semi-natural coastal woodlands characterised by their by Ash and Wych Elm canopy domination. Unfortunately, many of the Elms have succumbed to Dutch Elm disease in recent years However, a few can still be seen along the stream sides. The grasslands in the base of the valley are maintained for recreational use.

The coastal slopes comprise a mosaic of habitats including the nationally important paramaritime Magnesian Limestone grasslands that support a rich variety of wildlife. Notable species here include Sea Plantain, Thrift and Bloody Crane's-bill.

The sand dunes are of particular interest for their species-rich flora and include many nationally scarce species including Rush-leaved Fescue and Spring Cinquefoil. The beach supports an internationally important breeding population of Little Tern during late spring and summer.

Location
Crimdon Dene can be accessed from the A1086 between Hartlepool and Blackhall Rocks at grid reference NZ 478 372. Ample car parking can be found at the promenade overlooking the beach.

General information
Grid ref NZ478372
OS Explorer Map no. 306

The dene is managed by Easington District Council and further information is available on Easington DC website.

photo: www.wildstock.co.uk

Crimdon sand dunes

Cassop Vale

Tunstall Hills

Cassop Vale

National Nature Reserve

Description

Cassop Vale offers a unique opportunity to see primary Magnesian Limestone grassland, scrub, ancient limestone woodland and wetland on one site. The woodlands have Bird's Nest Orchid, Bluebell and other typical woodland plants; the grasslands support the full range of Magnesian Limestone grassland species, with Moonwort, Frog Orchid and Globe Flower. Northern Brown Argus Butterfly can also be found.

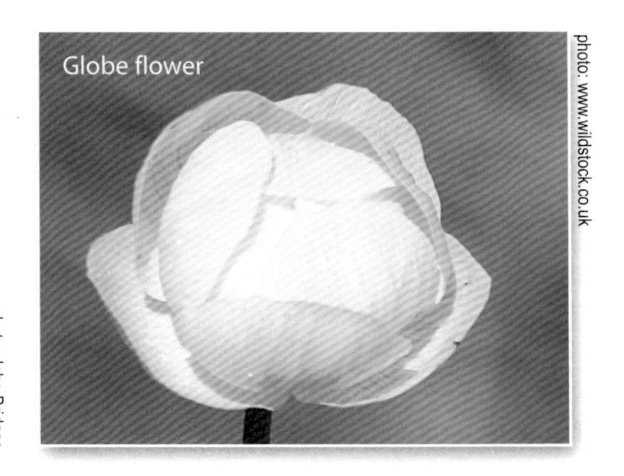

Globe flower

photo: www.wildstock.co.uk

Location
The reserve is five miles south east of Durham City on the edge of Cassop village. The reserve entrance is immediately opposite the Cassop village post office with parking in the village.

General information
Grid Ref: NZ335387
OS Explorer map no. 305

Managed by Natural England.
Full details can be found on the NE website.

Tunstall Hills

Local Nature Reserve

Description
Thes prominent hills mark the outcrop of the ancient barrier reef and include internationally famous exposures of fossiliferous reef limestones. They support a typical limestone flora including, Blue Moor Grass, Common Rockrose, Small Scabious, Frog Orchid, Bee Orchid and Autumn Gentian. The reserve is also good for butterflies such as Dingy Skipper and Common Blue.

Location
About 2 miles south of Sunderland city centre and accessible on foot from Ashbrooke, Grangetown, Ryhope and Tunstall.

Car parking is reached by turning up the track to Tunstall Hills allotments from Leechmere Road, and parking at the Changing Rooms car park.

General Information
Grid ref NZ395543
OS Explorer Map no. 308

Tunstall Hills are managed by Sunderland City Council and further details can be obtained from their website.

Castle Eden Dene

National Nature Reserve

Description
Castle Eden Dene is the largest area of semi-natural woodland in North East England. It occupies a steep-sided ravine cut through glacial deposits deep into the Magnesian Limestone. The dene vegetation is a survivor of the wild wood which once covered most of Britain.

Over 450 species of plant have been recorded in the wood, many of which are typical of ancient woodlands that date back to pre-medieval times. Spring flowers include Bluebell, Primrose, Wood Anemone, Ramsons and Early Purple Orchid. Rare and unusual plants found in the dene are Birds Nest Orchid, Herb Paris and Lily Of The Valley. Amongst the ancient trees can be found Yew, Oak, Ash and Wych Elm along with an

photo: Dave Mitchell

Castle Eden Dene

understorey of Hazel, Guelder Rose, Privet, Dogwood and Spindle.

The dene also supports Blomer's Rivulet moth.

The dene mouth has calcareous to neutral grasslands with Bloody Cranesbill on the slopes and Pale St John's-wort in the meadow. The two famous historical colonies of the Northern Brown Argus butterfly are still present and Slowworms have recently been recorded.

Location
Car parking and visitor centre are at Oakerside Dene Lodge in Peterlee, the reserve is sign posted from the A19 and from Peterlee town centre.

General Information
Grid Ref: NZ428393
OS Explorer map no. 308

The reserve is managed by Natural England and further details can be found on the NE website.

Photography

www.wildstock.co.uk contact: Darin Smith
email: info@wildstock.co.uk

John Bridges
www.northeastwildlife.co.uk

Magnesian Limestone cliffs near Crimdon

Natural England
Quadrant
Newburn Riverside
Newcastle upon Tyne
NE15 8NZ

Tel: 0191 2295500
www.naturalengland.org.uk

National Trust
Souter Lighthouse
Coast Road
Whitburn
Sunderland
Tyne and Wear
SR6 7NH

Tel: 0191 5293161
www.nationaltrust.org.uk

Durham Heritage Coast
C/O Environment
Durham County Council
County Hall
Durham DH1 5UQ

Tel: 0191 383 3351
www.durhamheritagecoast.org

Durham County Council
Durham County Council
County Hall
Durham
DH1 5UL

Tel: 0191 3834567
www.durham.gov.uk

South Tyneside Council
Town Hall & Civic Offices
Westoe Road
South Shields
Tyne and Wear
NE33 2RL

Tel: 0191 4271717
www.southtyneside.info

Sunderland City Council
Civic Centre
Burdon Road
Sunderland
SR2 7DN

Tel: 0191 5205555
www.sunderland.gov.uk

District of Easington
Council Offices
Seaside Lane
Easington
Co. Durham
SR8 3TN

Tel: 0191 5270501
www.easington.gov.uk

Durham Wildlife Trust
Rainton Meadows
Chilton Moor
Houghton-le-Spring
Tyne & Wear
DH4 6PU

Tel: 0191 5843112
www.durhamwildlifetrust.org.uk

Durham Biodiversity Partnership
Rainton Meadows
Chilton Moor
Houghton-le-Spring
Tyne & Wear
DH4 6PU

Tel: 0191 5843112
www.durhambiodiversity.org.uk

photo: www.wildstock.co.uk

MAGical Meadows is funded by Natural England through Defra's Aggregates Levy Sustainability Fund.

MAGical Meadows is a partnership of the following organisations: City of Durham Council, City of Sunderland, Defra, District of Easington Council, Durham Biodiversity Partnership, Durham County Council, Durham Heritage Coast, Durham University, Durham Wildlife Trust, Natural England, Sedgefield Borough Council, South Tyneside Council, The National Trust and Tyne Tees Farming and Wildlife Advisory Group.